The
ISLANDS
OF

❋ E,
❋ CONO, &
❋ MY

The
ISLANDS OF

*E,
*CONO, &
*MY

A Fable of a World Beset by
Economic Problems from Which
It Almost Escapes

BY SIMON RAMO

CROWN PUBLISHERS, INC.   NEW YORK

The characters in this book are entirely fictitious
and no identification with any real nation, living or dead,
is intended and none should be inferred, though similarities
are not coincidental since the leading characters were formed
from observations of the workings of many real-life nations.

Acknowledgment

THE AUTHOR acknowledges the aid given to him by a number of businessmen, economists, scientists, and philosophers with whom he discussed the key points that appear in this book, who made numerous suggestions (many of which the author understood, most of which he tried to incorporate, many of which he could not for the reason that in those instances the separate advices were totally in opposition), and yet whose names should not be mentioned because this would appear to lay upon them some responsibility for the way matters finally worked out.*

* Open acknowledgment is due Michael M. Murphy, a teacher of economics in the California State Colleges, who read and studied every detail of the book in its first draft and prepared critical comment helpful to the author in his first attempt to attain soundness in the final manuscript.

Contents

"A little money, like a little learning, is a dangerous thing, but much less perilous than abject poverty or total ignorance."

Sabio Cono—1740

The
ISLANDS
OF

 E,

 CONO, &

 MY

Chapter I

An Economical Fable

THIS IS AN ECONOMICAL FABLE. Not economical because it is cheap or efficient or is sure to produce a rich return on the investment of either the author in writing or the reader reading it. Rather, economical the way some novels are historical.

In a historical novel the characters may never have existed in real life. Numerous plot details may be free inventions of the author. He may choose names and places, produce conversations and confrontations, out of his imagination. All this makes the writing a novel. Further, the story may have been written for any of many purposes other than to teach history. Perhaps it was to explore new interpretations of significant events of the past, or to use the drama of truth to entertain, or to make a lot of money (in which case the author may have injected explicit sex passages not all of which happened precisely as described). Unless, however, the book stems from sound historical roots, it is not to be categorized with historical novels. It is straight fiction.

The plot of our recital, the environment in which the

events take place, the people, their involvements with one another and with their surroundings—none is tied to actual happenings. If they are seen to have similarity to the workings of man's real-life society on earth in the past or present, this is of minor interest to us, except in one particular, and in this it concerns us greatly.

We want the development of our fictitious scenario to recognize and respect economic wisdom.

Chapter II

Three—The Minimum Number of Characters for the Plot

IMAGINE TWO PEOPLE alone on a desert island and we have postulated automatically that a social problem will exist there. Quarreling or cooperating, they will be engaged in social interaction. Even were they to go to opposite ends of the island and ignore each other completely from then on, we would list this occurrence as evidence of a social difficulty and a particular way they chose to handle it.

Raise the number of our islanders to three and the opportunities increase immensely, much more than in the ratio of three to two. We now have added generously to the range of alternatives and decisions for each participant, the variety and number of contests and adjustments, and the potential competitions between order and chaos, love and hate, reason and passion.

Suppose next an ensemble of many people. Now individual activity alone does not dominate the society. Group behavior becomes important. Some new aspects of the workings of the society begin to unfold, including those involving the management of the affairs of industry, government, and the community life as a whole. More particularly, it is only when we have a group, and perhaps a large one at that, that it begins to be interesting and profitable to try to understand the relationships affecting the control and use of resources, the production, distribution, and consumption of goods, and organization to satisfy the needs of many.

But always we must be interested in the individual's tie to the group and our desire to understand how the group should arrange its affairs is really a manifestation of our curiosity about the human being and the human society. If we wish to learn something about economics, it is because, even more, we wish to learn about man.

Suppose, by some magic, we could be privileged to observe a collection of people coming together to live on an isolated island and form there a society. Even if we assume that the people we allow to land are carefully selected to ensure they are intelligent—also, compatible, mutually sup- porting as to skills and goals and philosophy, vigorous, ready to expand population and develop the resources around them—they will surely encounter the very issues we wish to explore. They will have to decide on rules and controls, including some regarding production and distribution, use of the land, their government's relation to whatever degree and kind of free enterprise they choose, on money supply, on the rights and obligations of the individual vis-à-vis the commu- nity, on ownership of property and other forms of wealth. In no way could they avoid the creation of an economy. If they have a society, they have an economy.

We want to stand offshore or above, observing but unobserved, watching the economy take form, grow, perhaps get sick and be made healthy again, be attacked and worried over by its citizen participants, and be constantly reshaped and expanded. We want to see exposed its facets and mys- teries, its predictable characteristics and its unpredictable dilemmas.

The plot of our economical fable will demand more

than a single character, more than one such island group, for we shall wish to see cooperation and confrontation between characters, that is, between societies. Then new dimensions of the problem will emerge; the scenario is broadened; the panorama of events is more colorful and exciting, and it tells us more. In fact, for the reasons noted earlier when we discussed individuals, a minimum number of three is again required—three islands, each impinging socially on the other two yet each also with a high degree of independent action. With three islands we can provide a real life drama of alternatives, competitive forces, and juxtapositions, and tilts and balance in their contests. We can engage in numerous recastings of the three characters in various, changing roles as participants, bystanders, referees, followers, and leaders.

Now, how do we arrange these three isolated, populated colonies? What plot, what intrigue, shall we invent whose unfolding will achieve our desired ends?

Chapter III

Three Populated Islands

IN THE YEAR 1740, several hundred carefully selected Spanish men, women, and children left their homeland intent on establishing a new and unique colony on the California coast. All went well on the high seas and at the resupply points along the eastern South American coast. But when the nine large ships passed through the Strait of Magellan and entered the South Pacific they encountered a storm of such duration and intensity as to throw them completely off course to the northwest. In an area about halfway along a line between Australia and the middle west coast of South America, the vessels, sails gone and coming apart at the joints, eventually ran into reefs extending from a group of islands.

The travelers were fortunate in being able to maneuver themselves and their supplies onto the shores before their ships disintegrated. On three islands, separated by about two hundred miles from one another, they established colonies—

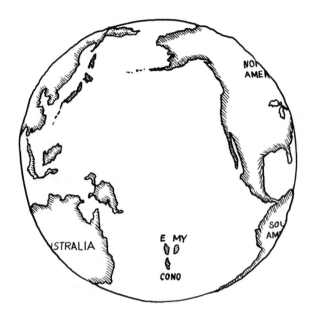

three independent ones, each group of travelers not knowing the other two also were saved and not too far off.

As we shall soon see, our colonists were only partially unlucky in this disaster. Using the know-how and materiel they had brought and the natural resources they found about them, they quickly settled down in their new environments to live healthily and reasonably happily and expand their populations.

They were unfortunate for one hundred years in that none of the residents of the three island cities could choose to leave and continue his journey to California or to communicate with the rest of the world. Why did they not build boats and survey the surrounding ocean? They had tools but no wood. Unluckily the islands had no trees, only low bushes. It took one hundred years before one of the three populations had so advanced its technology as to make possible the building of a vessel without wood with which the waters around the island could be investigated to a distance of some few hundred miles. It was through this technological advance in the year 1840 that the previously isolated islanders were able to discover and commence an "international" period of social and economic intercourse with one another.

We shall first tell the story of the period 1740–1840 in which three autonomous island states progressed in population, economic, technological, and social growth, each little national entity approaching its problems in solitary loneliness. This will be followed by a recital of the events of the next hundred years, 1840 to 1940, from the day the islands found and began to deal with one another to the point in time when the outside world (the United States Navy) first noted the three islands as mysterious echoes on its radar displays.

For two hundred years the islands were settled but unnoticed by the rest of the world. They were small both by comparison with the size of the entire South Pacific and when measured against the criteria that interested the world of that period. In the 1700s and 1800s, the excursions into the Pacific of Britain, France, Spain, and Portugal, with an occasional show of interest by the Dutch, were not at all for the purpose of seeking out small islands, especially those that might exist in the more southern areas of the huge expanse between America and the Orient. The Spanish had worked out a route to the East Indies, the Philippines, India, and East Asia, by land from the Atlantic across the Isthmus of Panama, north up the Pacific coast to Acapulco in Mexico and then straight west across the ocean to the Indies. This became the sensible route for everyone, considering weather, wind for sailing, shortest distance, and ease of navigation.

It is true that Captain Cook was given the specific task of sailing around the tip of South America and looking over the broad South Pacific region "thoroughly." One objective of his was to prove or disprove the theory that a large land mass must exist south of Asia to balance the earth in the same way that South America counters North America and Africa compensates for Europe. Cook went south from South America and discovered the Antarctic land mass, then he zigged and zagged about the South Pacific until certain no large continent protruded in the region, nothing even as big as Australia, which everyone then considered quite uninteresting.

When looking in a huge haystack for a large tank or at least a crowbar, one does not examine the straw finely, as one would need to do if looking for a needle. Cook checked out several tens of millions of square miles of ocean searching for large continents. Each of our three islands represented less than a hundred square miles, little more than a millionth of his haystack. Had he passed by one closely he would hardly have bothered to note it in his diary. Were he bent on seeking out and tabulating every such tiny spot in the vast region he was surveying, he would still be zigging and zagging today.

After the Panama Canal was built the world had even less reason to sail out to find and explore small land masses in the waters near the three islands. Still less was there incentive for those intent on commercial trade to go wandering about the area, lying as it did thousands of miles off the trade routes. More than enough small islands were available on direct sail from Acapulco to the Indies to satisfy the interest of the few dillydalliers who occasionally participated in the voyages. Sailors with a taste for such trivial island exploration were greatly outnumbered by those who had more practical things on their minds, such as Oriental products for profitable exploitation.

In the late 1930s, American and Japanese naval activities, including air scouting, began to cover large areas of the Pacific, looking for, and little else, each other. Only about then was it possible to note the pollutant in the sky accidentally and to become curious about where it was coming from. Furthermore, at around this time, radar apparatus began to appear on the United States Navy ships and planes that were searching the seas and the skies. The radar watchers had a professional interest in checking on signals that they judged spurious at first but that insisted on registering repetitive readings as to location.

And so our fable is equipped now with three tiny nations that for one hundred years will grow separately and for another hundred years will grow in cooperation and conflict with one another, all in isolation from the rest of society. We shall have an opportunity to look at both domestic and international economics. But what happened to them in two hundred years would perhaps prove quite uninteresting to us if it were not for the very unusual way in which the colonization plan had been worked out from the beginning and the rather remarkable job of selecting the people, fitting out the vessels, and handling every other aspect of organizing the expedition.

The man who put together the project and directed it, Cono, will prove extraordinary to us in two ways. First, the thinking he did that led to the program turns out to fit perfectly with the needs of our economical novel. The people— men, women, and children—were chosen for this trip for their vigor, skills, ideas, family background (for their genes, we would now say), and their susceptibility to the indoctrination which Cono insisted upon. Cono had in mind no ordinary colony. In setting out to establish a microsociety in the new land of Spanish California, he wished to attain a form of civilization, a political, social, and economic entity, in consonance with his own carefully analyzed and treasured concepts.

His thorough planning included dealing with the possibility of difficulties during the voyage and the loss of people and supplies along the way. With two other leaders in addition to himself, he divided the nine ships into three trios, each group under one of the leaders. He arranged points for rendezvous and resupply along the South American coast where, if the nine ships were separated, they might hope to come together again. He invented techniques of signaling to try to keep all nine ships together, or in the event bad weather precluded this, to keep the ships within each of the three trios locked at least with their two fellow group members. His choice of the number of ships and his assigning of individuals, animals, and equipment to each of them were based on the idea of redundancy for protection. He wanted his mission to survive even if some of his ships were lost.

Of course, he did not count on a storm so severe as to totally disrupt the mission. In particular, it had not occurred to Cono that his zeal to establish a new economic entity would lead to its being realized through circumstances he probably would have considered catastrophic had he imagined them before leaving Spain. The unexpected isolation of the colonies on the islands afforded opportunities to develop the kind of economy he wanted to an extent well beyond his contemplated colony in California. There he would have been forced to compromise his real desire in order to allow for the continued and necessary tie to the Spanish homeland, its government and culture, and especially, its economics, which Cono had viewed with little admiration.

But we said there are two ways in which Mr. Cono is important to us. We use the present tense here deliberately. Because of a special accident of fate, we shall benefit by having available to relate our tale a thoughtful and highly interested analyst, one who is not preoccupied with other duties and can devote full time to seeing, deliberating upon, and then elucidating for us the developing patterns of the society on the islands. Fortunately for us now as we start our story, though regretted by his associates at the time, Cono was the only person of the several hundred men, women, and children who failed to survive the storm. At the height of it, he was most often on deck, standing in precarious spots, busily giving orders, making firsthand observations, and miraculously keeping his poise. As luck would have it, after the peak passed, he was careless while passing a damaged edge of the side framing and a wave of unexceptional force and size caught him off balance and swept him away suddenly. As the voyagers became island residents, Cono, from above, with little on his schedule but an occasional harp lesson, was able to put his total brainpower to the task which interests us.

Now we wish rather urgently to get to the islands, their settling, their developing of a society from which, with Cono's commentary, we can learn much. But first we must hear more about how Cono brought the whole expedition about. Without understanding the plans he conjured up, it would seem quite incredible that the islands came to match so beautifully the objectives of our economical fable.

Chapter IV

Cono and His Game Plan

MY NAME IS CONO and I am (or was, that is) a citizen of Spain. Though only forty years old when I started planning my California colony, I was already the head of one of the wealthiest and most influential families in all of Spain. I was a direct descendant of the first Cono, a Marrano who took the name in 1492 as he escaped the Inquisition and preserved his assets and position by assimilating completely into the Latin domination of Spain.

My family had been active in many fields well beyond the merchant operations of the first Cono and his ancestors before him. I personally greatly broadened the family operations since assuming command at an early age when my adventuresome father was lost viewing experiments in our explosives laboratories at too close range. However, for over one hundred years before I took control, we had already expanded into manufacturing, exporting, and importing. We operated the largest private fleet of ships in Europe, using them particularly for the transportation of people and goods to and from Europe and the Spanish possessions in the New World. My grandfather had enlarged our activities to include the production of ships for military and commercial purposes, and my father set up factories, which I greatly expanded, for production of metallic and wooden products such as tools, guns, instruments, and machines for woodworking, textile-weaving, and glassmaking. In the last several decades our family added greatly to our wealth by broad technological efforts in chemistry and metallurgy and by bringing precious metals and special chemicals from America to the rest of Europe through Spain.

My position in the Royal Court was strong and this not alone because I was rich. My influence was based on the wide range of my business involvements, most of them vital to the health of Spain, and on the breadth of my personal interests as well.

If the way I have presented this quick summary appears to you to constitute evidence of conceit, let me hasten to admit that I was helped in my exploits by good fortune. The best example of this was my close friendship with José Patiño. He was the King's Managerial Minister, actually his principal aide, and also an intellectual, an economist. Patiño was powerful in Spanish government decisions during the very years when I was planning my project and he aided in arranging government approval for it.

During the period (1720 to 1740) that directly preceded my expedition to California, Spain was constantly at war with Britain and often with other nations on the Continent. It was not only that my industrial and shipping operations and my technological research investigations were critical to the throne during these years. Also, my performance was better than competitors'. British rivalry in exploiting American possessions was growing ever more troublesome. Spanish ships carrying freight from America were frequenty intercepted, but not mine. Schedules slipped in shipping and production, costs ran above estimates, and technology lagged in Spain, but not in my companies. This was not the result of magic or luck. I did a better job of management. I paid more attention to strategy and detail, to training and organization. The Crown recognized this and appreciated it.

I knew it was commonly said in Court circles and in industrial and professional fraternities that "Cono is a very learned man." I do not know if I deserved that description but certainly I had great curiosity about the goings-on in science and technology, and my home was the scene of a steady stream of symposia on economics, industrial management, and organizational theory. I participated actively in these sessions. Even allowing for the special courtesies due the host, particularly one so influential as I had become, my comments were taken seriously and respected by the other participants to an extent which gave me encouragement and satisfaction. Economics and politics went hand in hand with me and I went mind in mind with my friend Patiño. His thinking closely paralleled mine as to changes needed if Spain were to improve its economy, its stature among nations, and its security in an increasingly dangerous world.

King Philip and Patiño were keenly aware that the British colonies appeared to be making greater headway in America than the Spanish colonies. Spanish managers in America showed excellent results when they were "recruiting" and supervising native slave labor to extract valuable minerals and shipping them to Spain. Also, Spanish missionaries, aside from the approved task of bringing their religion to native Americans, organized the population along lines that suited the Spanish Court. These contributions by the miners and Spanish missionaries were appreciated. However, Spanish-born colonists were not arriving in substantial numbers to engage in creating rapidly growing Spanish-American states with the appearance of solid permanence. By comparison, England seemed to be much more successful in founding strong colonies of committed pioneers.

Particularly on the Pacific side of North America was Spain slow in developing its American territories. The leadership of Spain in the 1730 to 1740 period believed it needed urgently to settle more Spaniards in all of Spanish America, but especially along the west coast, if Spain were to hold on to its American possessions in the long term against aggressive England. Meanwhile, the Spanish economy was weak, and the constant warfare from which the country was unable to extricate itself precluded investment in economic growth in the mother country. In fact, almost the entire value of Spanish America to Spain was its ability to obtain and then sell, in exchange for required goods coming from elsewhere in Europe, the treasures being taken from the earth in America.

These factors were continually under serious discussion by the influential of Spain, at least by those that understood the problems, and, I have to say that, what with all of my Court contacts, my diversified commercial activities, and my wealth, all based in Spain, I was one who understood these matters well, perhaps better than anyone. But there is something else. It was part of my makeup that my thoughts dwelt on the alternatives for governing Spain, or any nation for that matter. I could not resist devoting time to the question of how best to realize a stable, growing, prospering economy. I felt ways must exist to organize the efforts of the people so the resources they command and the skills they possess, or might be caused to learn, could be used to attain something closer to their goals than I saw Spain achieving. I granted the permanent existence of national rivalry, the limitations inherent in man's greed, the continuing ignorance of most, the unavoidable poverty and disease, the unpredictable hazards of nature, and all the rest. Nevertheless, I believed Spain could do better.

I was particularly interested in the concept of free enterprise. Of course, I was accustomed to, and so allowed in my mind for a substantial amount of governmental control. But I wanted to give as much rein as possible to private, individual initiative. I wanted to see superior methods invented to accumulate capital and make it available to people with ideas and organizing skill, to use borrowing or credit advantageously, and to try to arrange for the fullest utilization of resources—human and physical.

Naturally, I discussed these matters with my friend Patiño. We both knew of the difficulty of trying to effect real changes in Spain. We could hardly hope to conduct major experiments in the running of the Spanish society in view of the overwhelming power and the unchangeable and negative nature of the Royal Court and the rest of the establishment, the lack of education and understanding of the people, and the emergency problems with which Spain was plagued, including, of course, its inability to get along with its neighbors.

Thus, it began to occur to me to try to set up a model community, starting from scratch. America was the available, open proving ground. Since I was personally in a position to finance the entire project and since the way I described my intentions fitted perfectly with the Court's desire to see a part of overall Spanish energies devoted to the accelerated colonizing of Spanish America, I found my program enthusiastically accepted. Patiño paved the way and the King's interest and cooperation grew as I developed my plan.

In some respects what I wanted to do was very straightforward. I arranged with the Court for the allocation to the proposed Cono Colony of a large amount of land in California. I proposed to select my colonists to make for maximum chance of success. I needed population growth and economic growth. I knew I must have compatibility, health, vigor, devotion, and determination on the part of the colonists. I wanted people of exceptional skill and, more especially, with the proper varieties of skill. I planned to choose gifted and specialized farmers for cotton, grain, and vegetable farming, experts in metallurgy and chemistry, those who knew how to produce glass and paper, cultivate seeds, make cloth, shoes, and clothes, educate children, be good parents and good citizens.

But I wanted more than this. I wanted people who

would understand my economic theories, who would be committed to the operating of a viable economic society. I wanted an enthusiastic interest in growth, ambition to prosper, and acceptance of the concept of reward for individual initiative. I would start with colonists holding a balanced view of the role of citizens, acting as a group and setting up their rules through elective government, on the one hand, yet prizing private enterprise with capital and savings at risk to realize profits, on the other.

I persuaded two other outstanding Spaniards to join me as deputies. My "chief scientist" was Mateo Yanez. He was a descendant of the great Hernando Yanez de la Almedina (who had studied under Leonardo da Vinci and had been the greatest artist of the Spanish Renaissance). Mateo Yanez (whom we shall henceforth refer to, as I always did, only by the acronym formed by his initials, MY),* was a leader in numerous aspects of science and engineering, his work ranging from structures, including ships, to machines for agriculture, glassmaking, papermaking, and textile fabrication. For all of these fields he had designed and built many original tools and instruments. He operated a gunmaking factory for the government and in his laboratories was surrounded by a large group of eager and talented apprentices. Much of his activities for twenty years had been underwritten by and performed for my industrial empire.

The third key member of the team—an ex-ship captain and a national hero as a result of a brilliant record on the seas, particularly in clashes with British ships in the Caribbean—was a skilled navigator, schooled in the planning and implementing of long voyages between Spain and America, a man widely respected for leadership, strength, competence, and integrity. His full name was Eduardo Emanuel Enrique Escobar Escocina Espinosa Esquival. I always called him Captain E for short.

I planned nine ships. There would be E, CONO, and

---

* The reader is advised to use the Spanish pronunciation for "MY," as in the English "me."

MY groups of three ships each, all to have similar full com-
plements of personnel, skills, apparatus, and materiel. (Two
donkeys, two goats, and two dozen chickens on each vessel.) With the full team meticulously selected, some with
wives and children, and with the ships very large and especially designed and built for the mission, I was ready to
launch my project.

We left Spain in 1740 with the blessings of the King. As
I sailed, not realizing how events would actually turn out, I
contemplated the handicap of my continuing ties to Spain
and decided to be optimistic. I knew I would have to deal
with the Court of Spain as I ran my colony, but so long as I
was the colony's governor I could shield the operations of my
model society from overly restrictive domination by the
homeland. At most, I would have to pay a slight penalty that
would tax the economy a little. I did not know what I would
find in the New World but I felt that my basic economic
theories would suffice to make it all work out successfully so
long as I had a cooperative, intelligent, enthusiastic ensemble
of people. It had not seriously occurred to me that I would
lose my life at sea. If it had, I would not have rated very high
the possibility that my role in afterlife would allow for a
continuation of my studies in economics.

Chapter V

Gold Money, Land Money, Nothing Money

IN MY PERCH above and beyond, I was both apprehensive and intrigued as I saw the islanders set about to settle and expand on the three islands, which I immediately named E, CONO, and MY, after the leaders. I was delighted, of course, to find that the colonists had been able to save machines, animals, and supplies, not to mention their lives, and had arrived at pleasant, warm islands, surrounded by plentiful, edible sea life, and copious well-watered soil for raising crops.

The islands were similar to one another, with mineral-rich, rocky coasts and high central plateaus covered by low bushes heavily laden with fruits and inhabited by pigs—small and wild yet accommodatingly slow and stupid enough to be easily caught—and large birds. From sea and land the people could with reasonable effort have meat, fat, skins, feathers, fruits, vegetables, grains, cotton, and linen. The lack of trees was in substantial part (if one forgets shipbuilding) compensated for by oil, almost as readily tapped by digging holes near natural surface pools along the coasts as was the fresh water on the plateaus.

Clearly, the hundreds of colonists that had landed on each of the three islands could live well and have time to think and play. I could concentrate on worrying about their social-political-economic endeavors, or so I hoped. They would not forget my teachings, I was confident. Their brains' seasoning, my planting of concepts, had been thorough. The abandonment, at least for the near future, of a colony in California would not cause them to lose interest in creating an orderly society, one oriented to productivity and growth and to the fullest utilization of individual and common resources.

On the ocean and for a period after the shipwreck, the islanders had operated under a social system that could hardly be described as free enterprise, capitalistic, and democratic. During the voyage the captain of the ship was very much in total command. After the landings on the islands, everyone received his share from a common pool of food and other resources. No great incentive existed for any individual to be diligent rather than lazy in the performing of his assigned duties. He would receive his share of the common pool in either case. The islanders did not start out operating with a profit incentive, whereby each person receives goods in direct proportion to the value of what he produces. Individuals were not engaged in maximizing profit by seeking to produce that which would most efficiently satisfy the desires of the population around him. People did not move to preferred occupations because of the incentives for increased production. The land of the island was publicly owned, as far as the impact on the people was concerned. Everyone assumed he had an equal right to the produce of the land.

But the islanders had been trained by me. They were certain, to use my words, "that all resources will be best employed, and everyone will do that which makes the most sense for the good of all, if there is a profit motivation and free enterprise becomes the basic philosophy of the social and economic system. If everyone owns the land, then fruit will be harvested before it is ripe, for no person will leave berries on the vine for fear someone else will come and pick them. Similarly, a stream may be fished bare instead of properly conserved. Private ownership of land will mean the right balance between its use and its conservation. The free market will correct the errors of any central planner. Anyone not engaged in doing that which the market really wants will soon discover that he must change his ways or suffer in his standard of living. If a man spends his day fishing but can sell his fish only at a loss on his investment in time and equipment, then he is not using these resources as society would value them most. If another man spends his day making shoes and earns a great profit, it is because he has met the demands of the consumer. Thus, men seeking only their own profit are led indirectly to satisfy the desires and demands of the public."

In a few months after their arrival the islanders were organizing free-enterprise, capitalistic democracies.

I had not expected that one of the first problems on two of the islands would be their lack of money and their need for inventing around this lack. Their extemporizing on the money issue both surprised and worried me.

I had provided the project with a liberally packed box of gold coins to which was added any small reserves the travelers might have brought along, deposited with me for safekeeping during the voyage. One administrative assistant (I called him my "banker") on my principal ship was assigned to keep a list of the "deposits" of each traveler. When requested to do so, he good-naturedly also kept track of the little IOUs transacted amongst the travelers during their voyage. They all received their board and passage at no charge, of course, and a salary over and above this. This had to be entered into the books. During the voyage the colonists would trade with and perform chores for each other and make note of little debts incurred. When we put into shore to repair and resupply during the Atlantic part of the trip, my banker brought his records up to date and showed everyone what money was being held for him in my "bank," shifting the written entries

about to balance out all the claims of debts between individuals.

Thus it happened that when the three ships of my own
group arrived at their island, CONO, they had all the gold.
The E and MY colonists had none.

Within a very short time they all needed money. Even a
few hundred people engaged in serving one another—one
catching fish, another building or repairing homes or teach-
ing school or making shoes or cloth or planting cotton—all
found that a medium of exchange was necessary. As time
passed, population grew, and activities became more complex
and diverse, they needed to keep stricter and more formal
records of debts and payments instead of relying on loose,
informal notes or oral accounting. They required means to
establish credit, loans between people and sometimes from
the governments they had set up, that could be supervised by
accepted rules. They needed convenient ways to price goods
and services. So they had to invent some kind of money and
to control the creation and supply of it.

Perhaps I should pause to say that when I speak of
developments on the islands, when I tell you of my observations of the activities of the colonists, these will rarely involve
the depicting of a sudden, an hourly, or even of a daily event.
For instance, their appreciation of a need for money did not
form on a particular Saturday. Instead, it grew gradually, and
it matters little to us whether this was over a period of
months or years. The problem of money became clearer and
worse and it finally required handling.

On all three islands the population increased very rapidly. (Particularly on E. The good captain, E, a bachelor,
turned out to have been very active on his three ships, and
the younger men emulated their leader with only a slight
initial reluctance that they managed quickly to overcome.
When E's colonists arrived they had already planted the seeds
for a small population explosion without benefit of cere-
mony—at least of the verbal or written kind. To this day,
formal marriage has been, at most, optional amongst people

born on E.) From hundreds of carefully selected colonists on the islands, thousands were born in twenty years. Most of the colonists had been well selected by me for their potential in this regard and they proceeded to have many children, with the children they brought with them coupled together at the earliest possible age. Thus, for every pair of teenagers there were several such pairs two decades later. In forty years the population of the three islands was nearly 8,000; in sixty years, over 15,000; in eighty years, 30,000. When the islands discovered each other in 1840, almost 60,000 islanders were distributed about the three islands of E, CONO, and MY.

On the island of CONO, without my specific approval sought, my banker was directed to divide up my gold by families, taking some account of the size of the family unit. He performed the job and, with a slight amount of haggling and dissatisfaction, the banker entered a deposit in the bank for that amount under the name of each islander along with the deposits they already had from the voyage accounting book. Everyone agreed that the gold itself should remain securely in the box. It was now their gold. Everyone had money and a bank book to prove it.

At first, exchanges of money to carry on the work of the CONO islanders was done by bringing the necessary information to the banker, sometimes with the aid of written records, sometimes orally. A little later, they decided to collect a peculiar, not too common, tiny shell and give it an unusual stamping to provide quick cash for small exchanges. Then they made copper coins and still later paper currency. They began to formalize the written transactions between individuals and businesses, mainly, that is, they wrote checks that could be cashed at the bank based on signatures of depositors.

The central bank itself aided in this process by paying for the printing up of currency as soon as the papermakers had innovated a practical paper from the materials available on the island. The bank announced that this printed currency, the amount of gold it represented plainly marked on both sides of the bill, would be offered to any depositor at the bank at any time he so requested, up to the amount, of course, of his previous deposit of gold. The stated value of all the currency printed and in circulation initially was less than the gold actually in the vault. All accepted that the currency was every bit as good as the gold it represented. They came to the bank and withdrew from their deposits only the amount of such cash they really needed. It was better to keep money on deposit at the bank where it earned interest, write checks for large transactions, and carry only enough cash for shopping convenience, or, in the business, for carrying on the daily transactions. Thus, CONO had a banking system and a money system with a "gold standard." The colonists knew that the currency and checks they received were backed up by gold in the vault of the bank.

All I am now telling you sounds very straightforward, and the money and banking activities on CONO worked about like this for a number of years. Then some difficulties developed with money and banking on CONO. But before we take this up, let us look at the money situation on the islands of E and MY.

On the island of E they had no gold coins, no money in the sense that they had come to think of money, and little indication that amongst the readily available minerals in the rocks of the island (iron, copper, nickel, lead) would be found the prized gold or silver which could serve adequately as money as it did back on the Spanish mainland. They knew they could produce some carefully sorted and marked shells or rocks or copper pieces to provide cheap "coins." Of course, they could print paper currency but this would be play money, not really valuable, not a substitute or a credible stand-in for gold.

Frankly, I worried about this a great deal from above and the citizens of E worried about it from their real-life position. They thought they had an answer. There really was something valuable on the island. It could be divided up and kept track of. Its ownership could be turned over to the bank and be listed for its owner as a deposit in the bank against which the bank could print currency upon request. Against their individually deposited amounts, the islanders of E could write their IOUs, i.e., their bank checks, and thus transfer money amongst themselves or their businesses as they traded services, articles, or food.

This valuable commodity was the land itself. On the island of E, they decided to use land value to make a money system. I do not want to suggest that only on E did the colonists realize that land had value. I should perhaps have mentioned, in telling you of CONO's money system, that the government on CONO assigned portions of land to be used for various needed activities. At first, just after landing, this was rent-free. Later the CONO government charged everyone a rental fee for the land he used for a workshop, a home, or a farm. Some parcels of land became the homes, farms, or places of business of specific families and initially were vaguely thought to belong to them. Soon, however, these holders of land were required by the government to pay rent or else buy it at a fair price. Thus it came about that, while most of the land on CONO remained government-owned, some of it was in private hands, traded about and rented by the owners.

But on the island of E, their government, searching for an answer to the problem of money, decided that land ownership would form an excellent base for a money supply, especially since they had no possibility of a gold standard. The land standard, as they envisaged it, would work something like this. The government would keep ownership to most of the land. However, it would place a value of a dollar* per acre as the beginning average value of the land and assign to each person one hundred acres, without saying which piece was his. In effect, each citizen received $100 in his bank account, with the requirement that he leave his land

---

* We shall use the word "dollar" for convenience as a translation for their word on the islands for their monetary unit.

ownership with the bank to stand behind the deposit. The $100 was in essence a loan from the government to each islander, with his land as security for his loan.

When I first observed this concept developing I quickly understood it—then almost just as quickly decided I did not. When I saw the printing of currency by the bank to provide the cash required by the public for their trade, I looked ahead to what might result and became alarmed. My discomfort applied not at all to the island of CONO with its gold standard. (I developed some worries about CONO later but not for the same reasons.) As to this land standard for E's currency, I raised a number of questions which I could not answer. In fact, to most of my queries, my pondering of tentative answers seemed to promise a developing confusion as regards money, banking, and economic growth for the island of E.

Had the government of E really solved anything with the use of land as a base for their money supply? It was not as though a man could come to the bank and demand his land. That was against the rules. In the first place, if he needed some cash to operate his business or to carry on his personal transactions, he could hardly take and use the land instead for cash, even if the bank gave him the clear ownership and control of it. Naturally, the bank needed to stand ready with printed currency and give it out on demand to its depositors, up to the amount of the deposit. However, the moment the bank refused to exchange land for currency, would not the whole scheme be exposed as nonsense, the equivalent of no standard or base at all for the money supply? The currency might be regarded suddenly as worthless by a reasonable citizen and this belief could spread and have severe repercussions on the usefulness of the currency, to say the least.

Surely, the islanders of E, I recognized, needed a convenient money supply, but was currency, when based on land one did not really possess, really money?

Besides, land, after all, was limited in quantity. Sooner or later, as the population increased, as technology advanced, as more food could be grown per acre and more products manufactured per square foot of space, the limited land would go up in value. Is not land a bit special in this regard? Gold could be discovered at any time, so its supply might increase. New and better ways to catch fish might be invented which would handle the problem of more fish for an increasing population. Improved tools could build houses and shoes or keep them in repair with less effort and hence less cost. But the available land was fixed in amount and was basic to the standard of living and the growth of the economy. Its real value was bound to grow. How would its increasing price on the true, free market jibe with its use as a currency standard? Besides, gold is gold and can have a price per ounce, but a general or average price for acreage that differs in characteristic from point to point on the island—what does such a price mean?

While I was having these doubts, I was for a while reassured, if puzzled, as I noticed that the E islanders seemed to use their currency successfully. They went about their business of fishing, growing crops, and distributing and eating the wild pigs, exchanging currency in quite a confident, stable way. The government collected currency as taxes and spent it for common services. The chemists and metallurgists, papermakers and glassmakers all were working and receiving money for so doing. The standard of living improved as expanding production of food, goods, and services more than kept pace with population expansion.

Apparently this works, I had to admit, although I was not certain why. "But will it last?" I asked. With larger numbers of people every year, all mostly active, earning money, needing to hold a bit of cash readily available and more in their deposits in the bank ready to be drawn on, will not the money supply have to go up proportionately? In another decade or so, where will the new money come from? If the currency represents land, and the land on deposit does not grow, how can the needed money supply grow? And now that I had progressed to such a clear question—a good question or a stupid one, but one I could not immediately answer—another inquiry surprisingly emerged: Would not CONO, with its fixed store of gold also not growing while its total money must increase, run into the same problem?

How similar suddenly did the situation of a money base appear on CONO and E! CONO had taken something of value, namely their gold, and, while keeping it securely in the possession of the government, had announced that it was being divided amongst the citizens. It gave each citizen a bank deposit to get him started with his little supply of money. It used these mere jottings-down as records in its deposit book of the evidence of this ownership by each citizen. It printed currency represented by that deposit which it made available to the citizens for their use as a medium of monetary exchange. This is what CONO did. Now what did E do that was so different?

E took land, divided it up, made records, said that it belonged to the citizens, gave them a start with their individual money supplies in precisely the same way, and all the while kept the land securely in the possession of the government. The government bank on CONO did not give up gold upon the demand of the depositors in place of the currency they held. The government bank of E did not give up land for its issued currency upon demand. Both the actual amount of gold and the amount of land were fixed in each instance and, yet, with the growth of the society, there would be the inevitable need for more money in circulation and in deposits at the bank, would there not? Where would the new money come from? Why were the citizens satisfied to accept and use currency that had such a loose tie with reality as to basic value? For that matter, who was to decide what was the real value of either gold or land? Why had I not seen all of this immediately?

Part of the answer developed before my eyes. The governments went ahead and printed the required additional money, just like that. Well, not really at random or carelessly, the way that sounds. The government banks made it

available as loans to those who both needed it and could prove that they would use that money to help create valuable assets. Also, the governments printed money to pay for government work and that put money in circulation.

On CONO, one enterprising glassblower, Stubanos, and his inventive fisherman brother-in-law, Dupon, produced thin glass fibers, dipped them into various chemicals and more molten glass and fused and twisted them into long cords. From these unusually strong, yet flexible strands they then created a fishing net far superior to cotton available ones. The result for Dupon was more fish to sell with less effort. The other fishermen wanted these nets. So a little production operation was set up. A loan from the bank provided a bank deposit for the new S-D Company against which it paid salaries in the form of paychecks to several teenagers who came to work in the new factory. The young employees took their checks to the bank and cashed them in for newly printed currency.

The money lent by the bank to S-D had increased the money supply of the island and this new money circulated around the system. There was something substantive to show for this little increment in the money supply. Fishermen possessed good nets. People, as a result of the invention and the financial backing to exploit it, had more fish to eat and they were in a better position to feed the additional mouths that regularly left their mothers' breasts ready to partake of chopped fish. The entrepreneurs and their assistants who had made the contribution had bigger bank deposits.

At first I was inclined to jump to the conclusion that the new deposits coming from bank borrowings and the added currency in circulation that followed were a pure dilution of the value of the currency. So also, I thought, was money printed and spent by the government to pay for roads, bridges, and schools, when they spent more than they collected in taxes. There was no more behind the total currency than before the expenditure or loan was made, so each printed bill, each dollar deposit, I figured, must somehow be worth less. When people discovered this, I reasoned, they would refuse to take the currency or, more accurately, they would expect more of it for everything that they had for sale that had real value. In other words, they would all raise their prices. This would be the beginning of an inflation stampede—the government printing more money, granting more loans, and setting corresponding new bank deposits for the debtors with the result always being a need to repeat the acts and repeat them again and again, to satisfy the rising prices.

What I saw in action, however, was not this at all. So I knew something was wrong about my analysis. The true experience was heartening. People did accept the currency as it grew in quantity on CONO and the economy grew. Here and there during the 1740s and '50s there was some inflation of prices on some products but no chaos resulted. All of this forced me to be more open-minded and try to understand the situation.

Of course, I guess I always partially appreciated that the total money supply on CONO in actuality was not the gold in the box in the government's vault. Certainly it was not the land ownership listed in the record book in the bank on the island of E either. It was both of these, yes, but it was somewhat more particularly the total bank deposits and the currency and coins in circulation amongst the people. What was real money? Apparently, it was what the people were willing to use and was hardly well measured by the gold, still less by the land—not when there were bank deposits increased by loans on the basis of which business plans and sales transactions, and government and household expenditures were based. It took a while, even recognizing all of this, for it to dawn on me that a bank really could increase the money supply merely by setting up loans. The government could decrease or enlarge the money in circulation by collecting taxes or spending money. I was right in my original conclusion that with a fixed amount of gold, or land, there was, in a sense, less and less backing for money in use as its supply was increased. However, I had to accept that the existence of backing of the money supply was not the dominant factor in the currency's being accepted, in determining whether a money or banking system would work for a society.

But I retained some stubborn reluctance to accept these realizations wholly. Perhaps, I said to myself, these systems work with a small group of people who are able to communicate well with one another and understand and keep track of what they are up to. But what will happen when the population of the islands reaches many thousands? What if, for instance, the bank became careless about loans, lent too much, increased the deposits too rapidly, made too much money available? Or the government spent far more than it collected in taxes? Would there not then be great difficulties?

In some ways, the creation of more money simply by the decision of the bank to grant a loan was at first even more mysterious and confusing to me than I have so far described. Consider the following chain of events. Pedro en Teristo receives a $100 loan at the bank, but the bank does not give him the $100 in currency. Rather, it puts a $100 deposit under his name. Pedro's plan is to buy equipment and materials and pay his workers by writing checks against his new bank account. Those who receive his checks deposit them to their accounts in the same bank. Of course, he expects to be paid by his customers and to deposit these receipts in his bank account. On the average, day in and day out, he expects to have close to $100 kept on deposit in the bank, sometimes having $120 or $130 and at other times only $50 or $60 in the account.

Now let us look at the consequences of the bank's having listed both a new $100 loan and a new $100 deposit for Pedro. The bank is mindful of the fact that each deposit of funds is an obligation of the bank to protect the funds, to have them available for withdrawal by the depositor if he so demands, and even to pay him some interest, perhaps, on the funds he has deposited if he meets the bank's rules about leaving most of his deposit for a substantial period. Each new deposit is in this sense, of course, a liability of the bank and not its asset. On the other hand, the bank knows it will realize its profits from the interest it charges on loans. We can understand that an inexperienced banker, if he were intent only on showing a maximum, quick profit, might have a very simple view of life's best strategy. First, he would say to himself, he should always try to arrange for the greatest amount of funds to be deposited with him. Then he should count on the high probability that only a very small portion of the depositors will suddenly demand their funds back. Furthermore, with the economy growing and with his monopoly of the banking business on the island, he should gamble that the deposits will steadily rise in volume.

He would then argue, still an optimist and a gambler (and especially if he was both and there were no outside controls over him) , that he should seek to negotiate a high dollar volume of loans out to the populace. This would give him that desired high interest income. In fact, he might judge that a proper total for his loans would be something very close to the total of funds deposited with him.

If this banker were confident that whenever he grants a loan the funds will be immediately deposited with him, then he is even likely to invent the idea of granting loans in order to set up the deposits. Thus, on the day Pedro en Teristo receives his $100 loan and also sets up a $100 deposit, the banker is quite comfortable. That afternoon, should Hernando Povertas ask for a similar loan and assuming his banker assesses his chances for repayment as excellent, the banker does not hesitate to add both to his list of loans and his list of deposits. The bank has, we see, engaged in creating money out of absolutely "thin air."

If the banker were a private individual, his livelihood, judgment in granting loans, and record of performance, all would be bound together. A banker overly eager to increase his fortunes, seeking to earn interest on every dollar under his control, may be led to bad decisions. A few bad loans or a slight faltering of the economy and he would suddenly not be able to pay depositors and so certainly could not attract new ones. He would become adequately cautious, perhaps conservative, in making loans. He would have to be almost certain that reserves of cash on hand would be sufficient to pay off depositors on demand even if some of his debtors should not be able to repay a loan when due. Depositors seeking a bank would look not only for a high rate of interest on their money but also for security, and they would expect that bank to keep ample liquid reserves. Free enterprise banking thus is seen to possess some built-in controls against arbitrary building up of the money supply through overextension of credit.

However, banks run by the government could be subject to political pressures to grant credit and thus, as I now was beginning to realize, could possess different motivations to increase the money supply. A government-run bank might refuse a private individual or company if either came around asking for a loan, but could that bank refuse the government itself in a request to set up a deposit? How would this work out, I wondered.

I must say that, though all these questions applied to both the island of CONO and E, intuitively I felt that CONO's gold standard would somehow come to its rescue if problems of money arose. But would it? This money matter was especially a point of concern to me because the situation on the islands represented a wide departure from what I had assumed would happen with money in the anticipated California colony. What with the remarkable Spanish experience elsewhere in America, I expected that my picked group would surely find gold in California. Why shouldn't there be some gold there? I went equipped with a store of gold coins to establish my colony because, as other ships would arrive later, ships of supply, or of more colonists, we would need some gold for trade, perhaps before we discovered any. I hoped to find, as a matter of fact, that my colony could develop various minerals, woods, chemicals, and other products for export quite apart from the discovery of gold. I had equated (more or less naively, I now realized) the gold supply to the money supply, and I thought both probably would increase more rapidly than the population. But now I was startled by the new phenomenon, this despite my considerable prior study of these matters, namely, a money supply which actually seemed to be dependent upon decisions by banks about giving out loans or by the government regarding its own budget. It depended upon the whim of the government in the printing of money.

The total money available on CONO in 1760, counting all the cash out in circulation and all the bank deposits, very substantially exceeded CONO's gold supply. There was no guarantee that if gold were demanded by the depositor (or land in the case of E) the bank could be accommodating, even if it chose to be. In both instances the money supply was increasing, yet based on gold or land, of fixed, nongrowing amount.

My further analysis of these matters and any further serious attempts on my part to anticipate what might happen in the future on the islands of CONO and E were delayed by my even greater concern as I viewed what was happening on the island of MY.

This was because on the island of MY there was no standard, no basis at all, for the printed money and the deposits in the bank. The people on that island, as their activities grew, found also that they could not be satisfied with barter trading and the circulating of informal IOUs between individuals and businesses. They also needed money. They had no gold. They either did not conceive, or rejected the idea, of using land as a base. The leadership of MY had allocated some land to the people, and kept most of it under government ownership and control. Just as on CONO and E, those who had bought land from the government had begun to trade it here and there for commodities and services and to rent it out to others occasionally and to charge rent.

MY did set up a money system in the simplest way possible. They knew they needed to make transactions and keep track of debts and have some convenient way to price things. So one day in 1742 they created a government bank and simply set up bank deposits, dollars in the bank, for everyone, choosing an amount that they thought would provide each citizen with enough ready funds for his needs a few months ahead, $100 each. How could they gauge this? What could they use as a basis for a price, say, for a fish, or the repair of one's home or a day's work or a pair of shoes? They simply started out remembering about what these things cost in Spain and blithely assumed the same price structure would suffice.

With each citizen having a deposit in the bank, he could obtain from the bank some printed currency and coins which the bank produced on demand as a withdrawal or charge against the initial deposit. He could write bank checks to others which the bank would honor with printed bills, provided he did not write it for more money than he had on deposit in his account.

It seemed to work. So I tried to figure out a rationale for its working. I reasoned that the essential quality of money that gives it its value is marketability. That is, so long as a person is certain that he will be able to buy what he wants with these funny slips of paper, then he will be willing to deliver his goods for them. The paper certificates are not valued for their own sake but because they have purchasing power. But where does this power come from, this marketability? It is certainly not something that can be granted by magic. Could the government pass laws to make people use the money? Yes, they could, but what would it accomplish?

For instance, if neither the shoemaker nor the fisherman had any real confidence in the money, they would arrange a deal between themselves to trade some fish for some shoes. Then if the law required that they use paper money for the transaction, they would, in a sort of clumsy way, apply a little arithmetic to the stated, government-edicted value of the money and figure out how much of it should change hands.

They would be using the money transaction merely to obey the law and it would have nothing whatever to do with the real trade that was going on which would be done still by barter. Since the money would be a participant only as a bothersome, irrelevant second transaction, the existence of such money would, in fact, hinder trade, adding to the cost and time required to negotiate it.

But the government on MY demonstrated that they did have the power to give this paper money I first thought was baseless a special position—I mean beyond simply asking for cooperation from the citizens to get the money system started. Everyone knew the government had to raise some money from all of the citizens so the government could perform some chores in the interest of all of them (water supply, waste removal, schools, roads, bridges). It would have to tax the people. The government announced it would accept as taxes the paper money that it printed. The moment a man knew that he could get his taxes paid by using this money, he wanted to be sure to have a certain amount of it, at least enough to pay for his taxes. That gave MY's currency value. Furthermore, the government bank paid interest on money deposited with it. Since the money was believed to have some marketability, an incentive existed to place it in the bank where the bank's interest would cause it to have more value when withdrawn at a later time.

The danger, or the inherent flaw, as I perceived it, is that a momentary loss of confidence in the value of the paper might quickly snowball to a total refusal of anyone to accept it. The government might then accept it as taxes but they might also have a revolution or at least a strike on their hands in trying to use the tax money to pay for anything. What if workers would not accept it as payment by the government when they worked on a bridge or the water supply. It is a strange situation where everyone has to play ball in order to have something to play ball with.

The citizens of MY did play ball and I soon began to stop worrying about a danger to the economy of MY in the use of this system, at least for a while. A key ingredient to success was that the government did not print and distribute an abundance of currency. It tried to and apparently happened to produce just the amount that people seemed to need, or very close to it. The government had done a rather competent and fair job of allocating the dollars to the bank deposits in the beginning, I guessed at the time. When I became smarter afterwards I reasoned they could not easily have gone totally wrong. You see, if the initial $100 deposits had been too high, then the citizens would have been tempted to go on a buying splurge with their newfound wealth. Then, since there would not have been enough available products to buy in like measure, they would soon have bid prices up. As they tried to shop, their abundant dollars competing for scarce supplies, prices would have risen to equalize supply and demand. They were lucky; they started with prices and an available supply of money in rather a good match to the availability of products and services and the demands of the community. It was not until somewhat later that problems began to arise.

At any rate, whether I had it figured out correctly or not, the islands of E, CONO, and MY entered 1750 with established money and banking systems. By 1760 a few thousand people were occupying the islands. They were mostly busy and productive, with growing physical assets, expanding technological development, increasing standard of living, all three of them operating with a good deal of free enterprise and not too much government interference. It sounds good as I tell it now. However, I think that until they reached a larger population and overall economic activity almost any system of money and banking would have sufficed. At least, this is what I now believe, in hindsight. These were basically cooperative and intelligent people. The influential ones knew one another well. Folks had their differences, but they set up judges and juries to handle problems in a fair manner. All were anxious to make the system work. Such a situation was bound to be temporary.

Chapter VI

The Panic of 1780
on CONO

To MY SURPRISE, it was the island of CONO, despite the gold standard for its currency, that first ran into a serious money problem. It was worse than serious and more than a money illness. In the year 1780 the island's entire economy was disrupted. Production fell off. Severe unemployment built up. The price structure collapsed. Fortunes were lost. The standard of living fell. There was great suffering among the population, irrational action by government, and emotional reactions on the part of the citizenry toward their government. It was almost two years before sensible action replaced confusion and discouragement.

That this happened first on CONO rather than E or MY may not be too important to us. Within a few years the other two islands lunged into similar severe depressions with all of the same symptoms, even though the nations were isolated from each other. So perhaps what happened was fundamentally not the result of the system of money, since they had different ones. As I have had occasion since to contemplate from above, it was probably due to many factors all acting together. It may have involved some common defects in all the slightly different free enterprise economies the three islands had set up. Was it, I asked myself, the consequence of the original indoctrination for which I was responsible? Had I failed to anticipate something basically weak about free enterprise?

The people on all three islands had pressed for rapid economic growth. I had lectured them to strive for that. All wanted expansion of the economy, to produce more, possess more, give the freest rein and greatest priority to conscientiousness and hard work and material satisfaction. Perhaps all of the rules were set up to cater to these ambitions and overlooked were the natural instabilities and limitations in judgment of individuals, businesses, consumers, and government.

When responding to opportunities or problems my colonists everywhere would have a tendency, owing to the shortcomings of their abilities and their knowledge, to overreact. They were easily disturbed if things did not go according to plan whether it was production at the factory, or wages or savings to be realized. In a free economy, or at least an almost free economy, results did not always work out as planned. An overcapacity to produce goods for the market was bound to arise from time to time or an oversupply created compared with the unforeseen, lower actual demand. This, when noticed, would set up a reaction to cut back on production. Such a step, if overdone, would result in an undersupply later compared with the later demand. These cycles, ups and downs, were to be expected. But CONO's 1780 panic was not merely a more severe downturn than the average. It was more than a temporary setback in the growth of the economy.

Whatever it was that hurt the economy, money and banking problems figured somehow in the act. They did so on all three islands. On CONO where the economy fell apart earliest, the first apparent symptom I noticed was a banking sickness unfolding in the beginning of the year 1780.

Why did it take until 1780, forty years, two generations

after the landing on the island? Probably had several thousand islanders arrived, set up a money system, and commenced the development of their economy, the crisis would have developed in a much shorter time. But as we commented earlier, a period was required on CONO before the population and the economy grew enough in size to exhibit the characteristics of a free economy. For years the settlers thought of themselves as joined together in a common cause. They were highly dependent upon one another and could communicate easily. However, after forty years of population expansion, a degree of anonymity had set in. By 1780 there were a few thousand people on CONO, men, women, and children, with an extraordinary amount of independence and participation by the children over fifteen, who came into responsibilities about then, taking on jobs, marrying, and commencing the building of families. By then, the team spirit, the "one big family" idea that had been dominant, gave way to the individual determination to improve one's lot, make a good living, or better, get rich, with the general interest of the island-state now secondary. Some even abandoned voting regularly in the elections for their leadership, so busy were they with handling the commitments they had made to build their businesses, invest their own or borrowed funds, and develop the technology and the island's resources.

The situation in 1780 was that the average CONO islander both had a deposit in the bank and owed some money. His bank deposit and the currency he had at home or in his business drawer in that year were greater than the year before and substantially greater than the year before that, and so on. The bank had printed additional currency as required by the growing population with its growing transactions and activities. It had lent money to the islanders which had increased their bank deposits. In total, relative to the beginning of the money supply back in 1740, and even as compared with 1760 or 1770, a very large money supply existed in 1780. In fact the money supply had grown even more rapidly than the population. I had observed this and I was not overly concerned. I had become accustomed to accepting that the money supply need not be the equivalent of the gold held in the box at the bank.

My early worry about what the bank would do if everyone came with his currency or his bankbook and demanded gold had almost been forgotten. For four decades it had never appeared to be of any concern to the islanders on CONO and had only been a private hang-up of mine. The islanders simply did not make such demands on the bank. It was understood the government would not give them gold anyway. Each depositor seemed to be comforted by the fact that the bank was the caretaker of his share of the true gold. It was there in the vault and there was little point in wanting to hold it in the hand or in one's mattress. CONO's people were not hoarders. Surplus funds should be invested. These citizens, we must remember, were committed to economic growth, to the fullest utilization of their funds to advance themselves.

More people equated to more money needed to carry on businesses and daily personal affairs, all of which required money transactions. With more population the government needed to spend more for schools and roads and sewage systems and water supplies, and it needed to collect more taxes. But why did the money on CONO grow more rapidly than the population? To answer this question we must notice that the islanders had not only built population but they had built resources. They invented techniques that had greatly increased their standard of living. They had developed fertilizers and farming tools and so had more food to eat for each hour's farm effort, and a greater variety of fish, vegetables, and grains. Their homes were better, still mostly constructed of stone or sand-based bricks, but increasingly with more glass and more wood substitutes made from glass, earth and oil, plastic substances developed by the scientists and engineers. They had worked out ingenious ways of using the lighter metals and plastics to construct wheels and carts. They developed metal rope and synthetic fabric structures for small boats suitable for moving food and materials along the shores, greatly aiding in developing and enjoying more of the islands.

Each CONO islander in 1780 had more personal goods than the average islander of 1760 or 1770. The shoemaker, fisherman, farmer, or metal parts manufacturer could show man-made physical resources, buildings and equipment and goods, that had been constructed with many man-hours of endeavor. Funds had been invested to create these assets. The assets had lasting value for a substantial period ahead before they were worn out or used up and had to be replaced. The islanders had become gradually more and more productive, and each year they were producing more per man of valuable equipment, materials, and know-how.

So one could judge that the island's assets, the value of all that the islanders owned, were made up no longer of just the island itself, the people's skills and cooperative good natures, and everything they landed with in 1740. Included now were all they had built up, conceived, learned to utilize, and possessed in 1780. The totality, if measured in dollars at the going 1780 rates for replacement, came to a very considerable sum. In fact, I added up roughly the value of everything that was placed in mortgage, in hock, to the bank. The total, I was glad to find, was definitely greater than all that the bank had lent. No wonder I had begun to be reasonably comfortable about the situation.

"CONO," I said to myself, "has a good monetary system. It expands the money supply as required by offering credit to those that are deserving. The island of CONO is getting richer and they have learned to use credit and adequate money to make it all possible, just as I had hoped. The gold sits in the vault as the foundation pillar of their money supply. This gold and the good, solid thinking of CONO's leaders had led to a money crop based upon the mother seed, the original gold supply." I was happy and proud. Then the panic hit.

Of course, I noted in the years 1740 to 1780 that every

once in a while the bank made a few errors of judgment. Businessmen would come in with proposals to expand, with very impressive recitals of what they would do—new ideas, perhaps, for the use of a technological advance, or perhaps just the expansion of a little factory in view of the apparently unfilled high demand for the products. They wanted to buy more materials and equipment. They needed to be able to pay the additional employees before the new products could be established and the distribution system beefed up so as to be able to market more goods and use the added sales income to cover the added expenses. The entrepreneurs' plan was that after a short while the receipts would be high enough to cover the bank loan and all of the new costs and a substantial profit would be netted. They would pay interest all the while. Bigger business generally meant using a larger amount of borrowed money coupled to the business's own, internal funds for the most efficient use of capital, to show the best profit return on the invested capital of the owners of the business.

If the bankers made a mistake in judging the situation, of course, they shared the consequences with the entrepreneur. The case of Lopez Del Gambol was typical. He found that the demand for his new product, an oil stove that was more efficient, was not what he thought it would be. Worse, to develop it took more time and money than he had estimated. It began to appear to the bank, if not to him, that he might not even be in a position to repay the loan. The bank moved in, called the loan, which Del Gambol could not repay, took over the business, declared our overly ambitious operator broke, and sold his available remaining assets to one of the competitors who had been more skillful or prudent or just luckier, and more particularly, had a near monopoly making oil stoves that worked and were cheap, though very smoky.

A businessman in that position, of course, might lose everything that he had. He also might be able to live through the episode, his losses not so severe as to rule out recovery.

The bank would lose, too. All this was fairly unimportant so long as the economy grew rapidly (as it did until about 1780) and the number of instances where such unsatisfactory circumstances arose was relatively rare. I observed that Del Gambol, clearly an overly zealous, greedy, and unwise individual who got himself into a severe financial fiasco of his own making, was able to get a job, obtain some help from his friends and family, and struggle back upon his feet. He started saving money and later became an independent businessman again, selling cheap, inefficient oil stoves successfully.

The economy grew and the ups and downs somehow adjusted themselves and did not apparently interfere with the growth. What then happened to cause all this to change in the year 1780? This is a question I had ample occasion to ask myself, not only as the depression commenced and turned into a panic, but also in the later years. Actually, I am not 100 percent sure today. I can describe it best by simply reciting the situation in early 1780 of a typical business, say, a manufacturer of clothes or housing materials or implements for agriculture or road building or transportation. As of 1780, most producers found suddenly that they could not sell what they had produced as easily as they always had. People seemed to have enough of many things. Apparently too much had been or was being produced. Seeds, shoes, cloth seemed to be in surplus supply. There had been, as I have already pointed out, many individual oversupply incidents that were cured in a short while by slowing production to balance better with demand. But in 1780, everything seemed to be in oversupply at once, or nearly so.

At the onset of the depression I noticed two strange aspects of the economy before I was aware of what they meant. Inventories on hand, in stores and factories, began to accumulate in unusually large piles, and unemployment began to rise—both of these before prices fell. You see, each store and producer at first assumed that he alone had a temporary drop in sales or an overly optimistic order or production plan. A fired worker assumed he was special, unluckily and temporarily out of work, but certain to find his new job right away. Initially then, no businesses dropped prices. If they had, and hurriedly, before unemployment and inventory buildup became broadly based and important, maybe the depression might have been averted. It was worth pondering for the future.

Faced with the inevitable need to reassess their potentials for future sales, all businesses began to cut back on their orders for materials and supplies and to fire employees. Of course, as order cancellations came in and notices to depart were given to employees (who, after all, were consumers as well) everyone resolved to buy less—businesses, government, and individuals. The government spending program, budgeted to cover the general needs of the population in 1780, had been based upon taxes anticipated to be collected in 1780 which, in turn, had been based upon expected 1780 profits and income by businesses and individuals. Seeing less income available in the period ahead, the government deferred various projects, the building of a new bank headquarters, for example, and a new school.

A big communications project for 1780 was cancelled, dislocating the plans of all the designers, suppliers, operators, and their employees. The project involved a network of many large drums and reflectors, the signals to be heard for miles, covering the entire island. The mining and metals companies, seeing a smaller requirement for materials for the production of various metal parts and pieces of equipment, put off building new furnaces planned to increase capacity and also cut their research budget. As another example, those who were engaged in obtaining the oil along the shores stopped an ambitious program. They had planned some expensive, large-scale efforts to dig deeper holes and get larger flows.

After two months of 1780, a large fraction of the islanders were out of work, some businesses were unable to repay their loans to the bank and many unemployed individuals who owed money on homes and furnishings bought on credit used up their savings and were desperate.

A typical business before the economic crash might have had $1,000 in cash or on deposit in the bank and a $5,000 collection of buildings, equipment, and completed or partially manufactured products not yet sold. Against this total of $6,000 of assets, the business had a loan of $3,000 from the bank. I thought of this as meaning that the $6,000 in total assets of the business was really put up by two partners, the bank and the business owner. The business owner had a true investment of his own of $3,000, which for a businessman on CONO in January 1780 made him a fairly respectable member of the establishment. By June he could sell the buildings or equipment or his products to few indeed and only at a great loss. They were, as to their immediate liquid value, almost valueless. So he possessed only the $1,000 deposit in the bank, yet he owed $3,000. The bank wiped out his deposit, told him he still owed (i.e., was in the hole for) $2,000 and, hence, bankrupt. They took away all of his assets, his building, equipment, and the rest, which the bank couldn't sell either. He and his employees were out of work.

In this way the banks wiped out a good part of the money supply in a few months. New loan activity almost disappeared, now rated as pretty discouraging for repayment, and many deposits were eliminated as well.

Such money as was in currency was not moving. I began to see that, for an economy to be viable, to grow, to be active, to satisfy the needs of its citizens, there was such a thing as velocity of the money supply as well as its quantity. People holding on to their currency because they did not wish to make purchases, the banks holding it but not lending it because of fear that the debtor might not later be in a position to pay back the loan, a retail establishment's salespeople handling little money during the day because of no sales interest by prospective customers, a wholesaler keeping what money he had, anxious to stay liquid rather than to place orders—these were all signs of a dying economy. Too little money and too little motion of it means high unemployment, too little capital investment, too low production, and, finally, too low a standard of living. It also means a generally low level of prices, in terms of currency, because despite low production (suggesting shortages on the market that might ordinarily force prices up) prices were determined even more by the large drop in supply of money, and velocity with which money circulated.

Now we must interrupt this recital of the way in which the economy of CONO was beginning to collapse in the first half of 1780 to describe another characteristic of life on the island of CONO, one on which we have not had previous occasion to focus our attention. We have spoken of "the bank," meaning the government bank, as though it were the only bank. Actually, there were numerous private banks on CONO in 1780 and they had existed for many years. By 1780 they were very important actors in the opening scenes of the depression.

Even as the islanders had landed on CONO, some of the citizens were already in debt to others. There was a little gambling, trading, selling of services, promises of delivery of assets from one to another. Some had great ideas and sold their plans to their shipmates who offered to be partners or backers. Within a few years on the island, promises to pay debts, loans between individuals and between individuals and businesses, and business and businesses, began to be a substantial part of money interactions. A few individuals and businesses soon found they were being sought out by others because of their excess funds available for loans.

Generally speaking, anyone with a need for money could go to the government bank and describe his assets and his plans. Assuming the bank decided these were sufficient and sound, he could expect the bank to set up a loan with a deposit in his name against which he could draw funds. He obtained the loan with his assets as security and he would pay the government-decreed rate of interest. But if he chose to, he could go instead to those private individuals or private businesses that had funds to lend out.

If his profits were a little higher than anticipated, or more than he needed to use for his individual needs or for his business, he could enter the private bank, temporarily deposit the surplus funds with them, and receive interest as reward or income. Some people had special personal relationships with those who ran the private banks. They liked dealing with them more than with the government bank where everything was impersonal, a bit bureaucratic, strictly by the rules. The private banks served the purpose of collecting money from people who had no compelling requirement for it and making it available to those who felt they needed it and wanted to spend it—that is, the private banks increased the motion, the velocity, the use of money. A bank operator, in the business for profit, becomes uncomfortable seeing a lot of funds on his accounting books every day. He works hard to find someone who wants it and can prove he can use it well, who deserves the bank's confidence as to his future, and to whom the money can be lent to bring in interest income to the bank.

At any rate, with the private bank setting up a "deposit" in the name of the business or individual who had made a loan, that debtor could now go about spending his money by writing checks which would be honored at that private bank. Other private banks took the checks too as good money and then simply went back to the original bank to collect. The private banks on CONO had good reputations. This was true even though the more sophisticated islanders who dealt often in money matters knew that a private bank typically might have much more money lent out than its own capital, that is, its net worth or true wealth (as indicated in part by its own deposits in the government bank). The important criterion was that a good private bank did not lend out more than its deposits. It always kept a reserve. But the total deposits were usually many times the investment of the owners of the bank.

Everyone on CONO seemed to respect the private banks and admired their leadership. The private banks were realizing profits from their banking and the owners were wealthy individuals. With total deposits greater than total loans, most observers felt the banks were following a conservative course. A banker with $25,000 invested in his business might have $500,000 on deposit and $425,000 out on loan, leaving a reserve on hand of $100,000. This was four times the invested capital, but only a fifth of the deposits entrusted to the bank. However, the private banks did not lend money out indiscriminately or allow their ability to supply needed cash to customers to fall too low. A private bank that took such risks would lose its position quickly in the free market. Depositors would put their money elsewhere.

Private banks on CONO, along with the government bank, were increasing the money supply greatly in the 1740 to 1780 period. As with the government bank, a private bank had only to make a loan, entering a deposit entry of like amount to the debtor's credit, to pump more money into the economy.

We return now to CONO's developing depression. The private bankers, not the government bank, found themselves in difficulty first as the economic collapse took form. The private banks had debtors that simply could not repay their loans as the economy swerved downward so steeply and suddenly in 1780. This condition could hardly be kept secret around the island even granted the inefficiency of its use of smoke, sunlight reflections, and acoustic drum signals for communication. Word of mouth, taking a few days to cover the island, was a sufficient mode of travel for such bad news.

The opinion got about that if anyone had deposited some of his business funds or his personal savings with a bank he had better run to get them out. A run happened first to one bank where a few key loan clients had gone bankrupt. Such assets as these ill-fated debtors had, that had been used as security to back up the loan, were taken over and quickly auctioned by the bank to raise what immediate cash the bank could. This sum turned out to total far less than the loan. Few were interested in buying the auctioned assets—buildings, equipment, materiel, partially finished goods—at any price. This led to more depositors demanding their deposited

funds back from the bank in a hurry. What depositors wanted, of course, was currency.

The first private bank, El Banco Fortuismo, that came under this kind of a siege closed in March 1780. After it ran out of cash, it wrote checks to its depositors against the El Banco Fortuismo's account on deposit in the government bank, quickly using up all of its funds there in response to its depositors' demands. When the money Fortuismo had in the government bank, a relatively small amount compared with its clients' deposits and loans, was used up, Fortuismo simply had to announce a "moratorium" on its payouts. It could not pay off any more depositors until and unless its debtors repaid loans or it realized something in cash as a result of selling off the assets of those who had pledged them on behalf of loans that were due but still unpaid or outstanding.

During March, runs occurred on most of the other private banks of CONO and many of them were broke by April 1. Even some that appeared in very sound shape to me by reasonable ways of judging also closed down. By "sound" I mean that their loans were very conservatively made, I believed, and they had a substantial amount of real wealth behind them as evidenced by their deposits in the government bank when the runs started. These funds were not as large as the total amount deposited with them and most of such deposits had been lent out. Still, the loans were made to businesses and individuals of considerable financial strength. Many of the loans were not yet due and callable. Given time, these sound banks could have been expected to have recovered cash from most of their loans outstanding. Then they could have paid off their depositors. But they could not do this immediately, on demand. With everyone wanting his deposit in currency, and many of the businesses who had loans due being unable suddenly to raise all the cash in view of their failing business activities, the banks had no choice but to close their tellers' cash windows and give depositors only written promises to pay later.

People began trading their private bank deposit receipts for whatever they could get in cash. Where a few months before a man could have written a $10 check on his private bank and obtained $10 in currency at the bank or $10 worth of fish at the fish market, he might now get his fish only if he offered a $100 check against his frozen bank deposit and then only because he knew the fisherman well and the fisherman was having a problem selling his fish. The value of deposits on record in closed private banks became almost worthless, being only promises to pay if the banks recovered in the future. Anyone that had currency was not about to part with it for any checks against untappable private bank deposits without an increasing discount.

All at once I realized that in all of my ponderings about money, what it really is, how it comes into being, what controls its supply, I had not adequately distinguished between different kinds of money. I could now see currency as one kind of money and demand deposits in the private banks as another. The first was going through a deflation and the second an inflation, both at the same time. As the situation developed, a printed bill of government currency, say, a dollar, could now buy a great deal more than before the panic started. The economy, like a balloon, had deflated. Everyone was trying to liquidate and sell off what he had to get currency dollars. Some desperately had to raise funds in order to avoid bankruptcy, and others did it because they were simply not able to sell their products at the original prices and kept dropping them until somebody would buy. People out of jobs decided they had better eat less and live less comfortably. Items of clothing already manufactured were being offered at ridiculously low prices. Food that would otherwise spoil was offered in June 1780 for a fraction of its earlier price. A glass pane could now be installed for much less money than before. With so many people unemployed, anyone who had work to offer could hire a competent person easily and pay him only a small fraction of the wages that had become more or less standard on the island before the economy came apart.

On the other hand, deposits in banks that were not liquid, represented by a check written against the bank, promising dollars at some vague future time, were worth much less than before the crash. In this kind of money, prices had shot way up, they had inflated greatly. The value of a dollar on deposit varied from bank to bank. For instance, at one point, the Fiv de Fifte Bank was honoring any checks written against its deposits at one half dollar in currency for each dollar called for on the check, with a promise to pay the other half later as its loans outstanding were paid off. Anticipating that that bank was in fair shape and would make some future payments, most sellers were willing to accept checks on the Fiv de Fifte Bank at about 60 percent of the stated dollar value as compared with currency dollars. At the same time another bank, the Diez Nationale Bank, was paying only 10 percent on any check presented to it against its deposits in hard currency, with the 90 percent remainder promised when possible. People took this relatively low immediate payoff to mean there was very little chance at all they would ever see any of the other 90 percent. So the Diez Nationale Bank checks brought only a tenth of a currency dollar per dollar deposit.

Now we must, of course, consider the government bank's situation in 1780. The worsening depression meant that the government bank itself had increasing defaults on its loans, with individuals, banks, and businesses either going broke or finding it difficult to pay their debts. The government bank's predicament developed somewhat later than that of the private banks, a little in March and April, in full swing by May. The government had to face the fact that a good part of its loans were to private banks, and these and other loans were backed up by what had become unmarketable assets. By June, the government, as a result of takeover, was a very large owner of businesses, private homes, and even pieces of land that had been in private ownership. These assets could hardly be sold to anyone.

Questions began to arise by mid-1780 as to whether the government bank could be considered safe and stable. I wondered about it, too, and in my anguish about what I saw happening my early concerns about the small supply of gold as against the large money supply arose again.

What, I asked myself again, does a deposit really mean at the government bank? What wealth does the bank have that it is safekeeping for the individuals or businesses that put that wealth there? On the good side, despite the many businesses and individuals that had defaulted on loans, the bank still had more assets than it had deposits. Or did it? If one counted at their original replacement cost all that the bank had come to own—industrial equipment, manufactured products, land, buildings—then the bank had a strong financial position. But it could hardly give these out to nervous depositors if they started a run on the government bank. Of course, the bank could print more currency to hand to the depositors if its small supply ran out, but what would the individuals or businesses do with this currency? Presumably, they already had as much currency as they needed. In fact, they now needed less because everything was cheaper. I assumed this meant that the currency would stay strong and the government bank had no problem of basic stability, hard as times were. But this assumption was a bit optimistic.

I had not adequately weighed the important factor of confidence, or rather the lack of it. The government bank made it clear that any deposit with it could always be demanded in currency. Now, the public recognized that the government bank could print currency as required, if it chose to do so. Actually, however, people did not know for sure what the government would do in a money crisis, in fact, *this* money crisis. They heard strong differences expressed by public leaders, all seeking solutions but also uncertain and wanting to stay in office.

For example, Jaime Derecho recommended that the government seek to limit the total of currency printed and in circulation to the amount of gold in the treasury. He went back to the original concept of a gold base and said the great expansion of the money supply through bank credit and currency printing to meet the requirements of an overexpanded economy was responsible for the depression. People had blown up their fortunes with imaginary figures on paper certificates and the banks' accounting books, and now the false structure had collapsed. Derecho did not say how he would pull the so-called "excess" currency back in. There was obviously too much in circulation by his criteria of the gold supply limitation. But with others talking almost the same way, some folks turned in their deposit books to the government bank for currency. They feared the government might soon refuse to issue any more.

The government bank withstood runs in May 1780 by printing currency amidst rumors they would soon stop.

Meanwhile, though production of many products had come to a virtual halt, the available inventory in most products still did not move very fast and prices kept falling in response to lowering demand born of no confidence and lack of money. The people still bought bread, though less, and the baker was not buying anything to increase his capacity. He bought flour, but less, and the wheat farmer and mill operators made no investments or expenditures they could avoid or postpone.

In July 1780, Marco de la Viva became the most powerful voice in the government. He had campaigned on a different promise, namely, to do something about the shortage of money. What he meant by this was not at all clear to me, but the majority of CONO voters apparently were sold by his approach. They looked upon themselves as having too little money, whether they were consumers or operators of businesses. They did not mean money on deposit in private banks which was bringing so little at the marketplace, but rather currency which they assumed would end their problems if they could get their hands on more.

I could see that Viva had a point. Production was down, unemployment was growing, demand had fallen and prices with it. If you assumed, and almost everyone did, that the value of illiquid demand deposit money in the banks would continue to fall, then the only money fundamental to the pace of the economy appeared to be the currency. Perhaps by somehow making more currency available to everyone the spell would be broken and people would start buying again, producers would be encouraged to plan for more production, and the demand would increase faster than production could get rolling, quickly using up the presently nonmoving stocks on hand. Then prices would go up, curbing the deflation that had taken place. People would begin to deposit their excess funds and the banks could begin to recuperate. My problem was that I was not certain how to do this. But I did not have the responsibility to work it out. Marco de la Viva had won out over the Derecho forces and he had the power of action.

He first ordered a drastic cutting of taxes, at the same time declaring a government "loan" to all citizens, printing currency as required and proceeding to distribute it. Almost instantly prices jumped up in terms of currency, inventories in the hands of merchants and factories began to fall rapidly as consumers and distributors hastily set out to gobble up everything they needed and could buy before it became unavailable. A wave of optimism suddenly took over and Viva was caught up in it. He decided he should add to the currency in circulation by a further distribution. This time he also made loans to the private banks and the purchasing power of checks written against the private banks' deposits suddenly arose as those banks announced partial thaws in the frozen deposits.

Viva thought he had a magic formula for curing both the deflation in prices when currency dollars were used and the inflation in prices when deposits dollars were used. But he had not anticipated his inability to control the price structure and the reactions of the people to these steps. In a matter of a few weeks CONO was engaged in an inflation raging out of control. People began to expect the government to print and distribute more currency momentarily. Orders placed were based on the conviction that prices rising so rapidly would be much higher in a matter of a few days or weeks when the payment would be made for the goods then received. No one wanted to hold off buying anything he needed, or might need later, feeling it would surely cost more then. All over the island people were making arrangements to anticipate the further rise in prices. Retailers, fearful they might not be able to replace their goods at the present prices—in fact, their suppliers were surely quoting higher ones—raised prices drastically. People bought anyway, figuring they ought to be well supplied against the coming period of still higher prices.

Of course, Viva found the economic boom he had started

could not be slowed by him or he would be in trouble. People were going back to work, the factories were beginning to function, and he had started to become some sort of a hero. His rival Derecho could not even get a speaking engagement to decry what was happening. So when the inevitable pressure for credit from the expanding industry built up he responded by forcing the government bank to lend money freely to the private banks so they could finance the buildup.

But the more he lent, the more currency he printed, the more he had to lend and print, and prices continued on up. It began to be apparent to all, even to Viva, that something was wrong. Viva thought he had merely gone too far but was basically right in trying to get the economy off dead center by increasing the money supply. His admission one day that he thought he must now start curbing credit and money supply threw the public into confusion and brought Derecho out of hiding. Many contracts to purchase future materials and equipment for the factories, and orders by the retailers far out into the future were cancelled in a week of emotion-guided collapse of the boom. People wondered how they could have let Viva talk them into another wave of over-expansion, boom and bust, this time even more disheartening.

People became demoralized and pessimistic as to the value of money all over again, but this time, in view of the rapid up and down in their spirits, the discouragement was very great. On the one hand, business had begun to get good, that is, anyone who wanted to sell something was temporarily able to do so if he were willing to take yesterday's price for it today. But on the other hand, he was afraid to because he did not know what his situation would be tomorrow, what he would be able to buy with the dollars the next day to meet his needs, to pay for materials coming in if he were a manufacturer or to buy his food if he were a worker. The citizens lost confidence in the currency. They were no longer concerned about deposits in the private banks which now had plenty of currency and could provide it to any depositor who wanted his deposit back. They looked upon the currency as mere paper printed in an indefinitely large quantity by the government at will. It was no longer tied to the gold as had originally been understood when currency was printed back in the 1740s. Derecho was right, they decided, and he now took command.

His temporary absence from the scene had given him some opportunity to think as well as to grouse. He now realized he could not take CONO back totally to a currency supply limited to the amount of stored gold. Especially, he could not do so in view of the expansion of the economy that Viva had created. He wanted to stay in office and he had to work fast to grab hold of the money supply and restore confidence in the currency.

He decided upon an ingenious, bold step in late 1780, when he came to power.

Originally, in 1740, when CONO set up its money system with initial bank deposits for everyone, gold had a stated value in dollars ($10 an ounce, it happened to be, mainly because this was an even figure that fitted the number of islanders and the amount of gold I had in my box. Each original islander was listed for ten ounces or $100 as it turned out, leaving some over for the government's treasury). Derecho decided now to change the value of gold in terms of CONO dollars. Having only about one-tenth as much gold as he felt was needed to handle the problem of confidence, and noting the severe devaluation in the buying power of a CONO dollar, he announced a new price for gold ten times higher in value. Instead of $10 per ounce, the government set a new value of $100 per ounce. He simply stated that this was what gold was worth in dollars. Most of my original gold pieces were used, under careful metallurgical control, to create new coins, each containing copper and lead and a small fraction of the gold. The bank gave out these coins for currency to anyone who came to its tellers' windows requesting the trade.

It was in this way that many depositors came to hold some of the new "semigold" coins and the absolute collapse of the money and banking system, and with it perhaps, the economy of CONO, was prevented in the early weeks of 1781.

Derecho then announced that the government would make no new loans; in fact, it would raise taxes and cut expenditures. Thus, he said, no need existed to print more currency, which was now pegged firmly to gold. Depositors could change their deposits or currency for gold to hold now. However, he offered government bonds at a good interest rate to anyone who had funds and would sooner earn interest on it than buy anything he did not need. Derecho said the inflation was over and more inflation need not be anticipated.

But there were repercussions. Unsolved problems remained and routes to certain economic recovery were as yet unclear. We shall want to come back to CONO and see how CONO worked its way out of the panic of 1780. First, however, we must skip ahead to see what happened on E and MY because, remember, they had no gold.

Chapter VII

The Big Depression,
E Style

WITH THE ISLAND of CONO well into its depression, I began
to feel that I understood why the island's economy had collapsed—in part, that is. I was still confused as to how many
factors were at play, how they were related one to the other,
which were the most important, which came first and caused
the others. Most importantly, I certainly was not clear on
how to keep the bad times from recurring. Maybe the whole
idea of an economy with private ownership of the means of
production and a free market for exchange of money, goods,
and services had been proved weak in theory and unacceptable in practice by the experience on CONO.

I had much to study, and I was worried. But my doubts
about free enterprise and CONO did not completely fill my
thinking time, of which I had a great deal, considering my
few compelling responsibilities. I increased my observations
and contemplations concerning the other two islands. I wondered why they had not gone into a similar chaotic economic
downturn and how, without a gold standard for their money,

they would fare in attempting control and recovery for their economies.

I had not long to wait. When their depressions began to take root, I could pick out the symptoms immediately, and I could readily ascertain that the timing had been decided by minor and accidental circumstances. MY and E, like CONO, were destined to be in trouble from a major economic depression. The evidence of this, I now realized, was present almost from the beginning of the operations of the economies on all three islands. I was just not a good enough economist to see it. In fact, I misinterpreted much of what I did observe, before the panic on CONO educated me.

For instance, there were those happy days on all three islands when the fishermen would bring in a remarkably large catch. With this unforeseen oversupply of fish, the price of fish would fall. Fishermen could not keep their prices up because the excess fish would simply spoil rather than be bought out at the usual price. To get rid of their inventories, the fish suppliers would drop their prices as low as required. People bought more fish with the prices low. They ate more and did what they could to keep the fish fresh for use over a longer period. There was a temporary lowering in the demand for and the purchase of other food products and even a temporary diminishing of attention to some other activities while the islanders engaged in mass fish smoking in an attempt to preserve as much of the big catch as possible.

I could see from such examples that supply and demand were keys to the price structure. Supply and demand underlay sales volume, profit (that is, the money made on invested capital), the income and savings of the citizens, and the deposits in the bank. It was evident that changes in supply and demand had wide repercussions. Thus, the price of other food products would drop because of the competition of the cheap fish. If it seemed that the higher catches might continue, this might even result in there being too many fishermen. A few of the younger assistants used in the fishing process might be laid off and have to seek jobs in some other occupation. Scientists and engineers might be reassigned to develop improved methods of preserving fish. So the disturbance to the economy from a deviation could be many-faceted and, in most instances, the economy automatically adjusted in a short time through counteractions that were set in motion.

Before CONO's panic, every variation in the economies I watched on the islands of E and MY, as well as on CONO, seemed to have a counter and the economy was thus self-adjusting, as I had hoped and claimed in my lectures. Typical were the entrepreneurs who occasionally overexpanded in relation to their actual potential. They relied too much on borrowed money and then sometimes failed to realize the expected volume of operations or the hoped-for profit on those operations, and thus were not able to pay back the loan or meet interest payments on it. Regularly, the banks on all three islands would encounter a few such setbacks and endure consequent losses. The individuals or the companies would go out of business or be bought out by their competitors, and the economy somehow would adjust for these rare events.

Similarly, do you recall how I had worried about there being an oversupply of money? This was almost as soon as I came to understand that creation of money could come through the banks' setting up new deposits in granting loans. Too much money in circulation would, of course, have the chance of chasing too few goods. Surely, if everyone were successful in borrowing money at the bank and everyone were still willing to honor all of the subsequent bank checks, then people would spend more. They might do it to increase the sizes of their businesses or just for their daily, more liberal, living expenses. But then the prices would automatically rise to neutralize this effect as the money-happy customers competed with one another for every product for sale. Too large an increase in the money supply would cause an inflation in prices, just about enough, I had thought, to neutralize the real impact of the oversupply and stop further inflation.

I observed, at least I thought I did, the same phenomena

with regard to the spending by the governments of the three islands. If the governments spent more than they collected in taxes—operated, that is, with a deficit in funds—they usually just printed extra currency for their own use. They paid for the goods and services they ordered with this new money, ignored the deficit, and incidentally increased the money supply. In principle, as a silly extreme, the government could order up so many big projects, if it so chose, as to employ every islander. It could pay each for his work with currency it printed, and then turn about and collect all of that pay back as taxes. It could then burn the currency and thus end up keeping the money supply from increasing. But then the islanders would all starve to death because there would be no money left in their hands to buy food and no one left to tend to the crops or do the fishing to produce food. I would resort to these ridiculous lines of thought occasionally as I tried to understand whether some action of government or business or individuals could be expected to have an important effect on the economy and, if so, whether for good or bad. In the instance of government spending, I pinned down in this way that government spending could cause inflation. The government could increase the money supply and drive up prices by coming into the market to compete for goods and services.

Similarly, I reasoned, if the economy were to slow up, if unemployment grew, people would be willing to work for lower wages, and be anxious to sell whatever goods they had for less, for whatever they might bring. Deflation would result, prices going lower what with too little money out and too much of goods for sale. Here, the government, by stepping in to purchase goods and services, could cause wages and prices to increase and, perhaps, could get the economy moving.

Again, if too much money was in circulation, the government could raise taxes and cut government spending and bring the excess dollars back out of the economy and into the treasury. Also, the government could hold back on loans to private banks, thus influencing them to make fewer new loans and stop increasing the money supply.

Do not think I was unmindful of these possibilities for government action before the depressions. Rather, if anything, I believed that surely either government action or else the automatic supply and demand effects and other free market compensatory phenomena would enter to neutralize and curb any mass runaway instabilities that might get started. I did not, at any time before the panic on CONO, really anticipate that an uncontrolled buildup of bad economic performance would reach the proportions it did on CONO. Yes, I granted, an individual might lose his job or his business through the ups and downs of market forces or his own misjudgments or poor luck. He would then find the dynamic effects of economic cycles catastrophic. But I felt that the average or overall effect on the whole economy would be a continual smoothing out of the ripples and contests. The result would be a growing, self-adjusting, free economy. I did not even take seriously any requirement for major interaction (that is, rescue operations) by government, even though I comprehended that government action was a factor in the workings of the economy. To put it finally: before the collapse, I saw no need for major deviations from the concepts I had conceived and lectured on as my free enterprise economy fundamentals.

An adequate anticipation by me of big economic instabilities and their potential consequences was delayed by the long time it took for the islands to build enough population and a large enough magnitude of activities to act statistically. As we have already discussed, it took forty years for free economy factors to control the society and override the personal relationships dominating the islands' economies. For years, everyone was acquainted with everyone else and what he was doing. Mutual assistance, independent of personal gain, was more important than doing business with one another. Quarrels were settled by judgments of peers, not by free market forces. Gradually, however, as new generations were born, as entrepreneurial activities became typical, as the islands were occupied and explored more fully, as miles separated families who did not see each other daily, the islands began to act as collections of independent operators, the individuals and groups negotiating and contesting with one another through free market forces. I was so wedded to my free enterprise ideas that I interpreted the progress on each of the three islands in those free enterprise terms, without noticing the human relations aspects.

The three islands began with differences in precise resources to exploit and in the nature of their populations and environments. However, and this was both worrisome and fascinating to me, when each island had come to operate as an essentially free enterprise society along the lines of my original concepts, then after a few decades its economy ran into the same kind of major difficulties that I had not anticipated. So we need not repeat the story—the overexpansion of money and particularly of debt and demand deposits in banks, the overexpansion of the idea of expansion, the businesses counting on increases in sales which were beyond the ability of the market to sustain, the bankruptcies and takeovers of assets by the banks, the severe unemployment, the collapse of the price structure, the runs on the banks, the loss of confidence in the banks and even in the society.

But we must explore some rather important differences. Let us take the island of E. You will recall that I left some questions dangling when I first told you of E's land-based money system. I confessed to you then that I did not understand it and I really had meant to ponder it all and determine in my own mind how it worked. It appeared that it did, but I had been concerned about the effect of a land-based currency on E's chance to build up a thriving free-enterprise economy along the lines of my teachings to E's founding citizens. Now, knowing that the panic struck there, we can no longer avoid examining how their money, banking, and land control systems were operating just ahead of the catastrophe.

In the 1740s, I wondered often whether E's land basis for their currency made any sense at all. Whenever someone deposited money with the bank, he obtained interest on it. The government said the interest it paid was just equal to a proper rental fee for the amount of land the dollars on deposit represented. The net result, so far as income on his savings went, was the same as though he really owned the land and rented it out. He was merely saved the job of finding someone to rent it to. Must businesses and individual families using land always rent it from the government? Can they never really possess and own it and use it as they choose and separately rent it to others for as much as the market will allow without going through the government as an agent? How does the government decide on the rent to be paid, or the interest on deposits in the bank, assuming they are really the same? And does not this overpowering government control of rent, interest, and land ownership constitute a severe handicap to a free-enterprise economy?

These questions were answered for me by the actual practice on E during the 1740s and 1750s. Citizens were allowed to use their money to buy land and some islanders did. They bought it from the government which periodically released some of the land for sale and set the price, always careful to put it high enough so not too much land was purchased and the government retained most of it in its "land" bank. Here and there, the islanders bought, sold, and rented land to each other, independently of the government. Thus, there was some land in private possession and some land in the government reserve that was tied into the currency and bank deposits.

How did the government decide on which land was to be sold to private owners and what its price should be? They spoke of an "average" price for land; then, usually anxious not to part with the land, insisted upon an above average price for a particular piece if the land contained any special advantages whatever, such as fertile soil for agriculture, or mineral or other resources, or easy access to fresh water or the ocean. If the land price was set too low, depositors would prefer buying land to other ways of using their money. Of course, the citizens could always keep their money in the bank and draw interest about equal to the rent they would get if they bought land and rented it. Why would anyone buy land, then? When would he regard the price as cheap? Perhaps he wanted the land for a business, one in which location or the specific resources on the land were important. Perhaps his investment in structures on the land was to be very high so he wanted permanent control of the ground under his facilities. Maybe he wanted to gamble on a rise in the price of the land and did not wish to depend on government action or decision with regard to his return on investment.

In sale of land by the government, we must remember that the initial rules were set up by a relatively small number of people. They tried always both to be fair and to anticipate the problem in the future of money supply and land use control. For a while, this motivation was key and helped greatly to keep things stable.

No matter how wise, objective, and imaginative were the shapers of these early rules, free market operations began to move in and affect this whole matter of valuations on land. Some unusually advantageous pieces of land happened to have been priced initially a little low. With the growth of population and activities, some of that private land began to acquire high rent potential. Hence, the free market price during a land sale was typically substantially higher than the so-called average government price for acreage set when the original money base was created. By 1750, some land had appreciated ten times in value over its price in the early 1740s. Moreover, it began to be realized, as years changed to decades, that a fixed supply of land was pitted against a growing economy and population. By 1760, the government stopped selling land to the people. One could keep what one had or sell it to others or to the government, but one could get no more from the government. That was the law.

The prices of most established goods remained about the same during the 1740s and 1750s, or fell as productivity increased in turning out the products. Wages rose slowly. There was little or no inflation. However, the amount of money in circulation and in deposits had to go up with the increasing size of the population and economy. It did so, as on CONO, through credit expansion, more bank loans, and government expenditures that exceeded taxes.

By the time 1760 arrived, I was still confused on the somewhat casual tie-in of rents to interest, land growing more expensive yearly, the government announcing annually an official new, higher price for "average" land per acre, but not offering any land for sale, average or otherwise. The government persisted in the idea, never mentioning that it might just conceivably be fiction, that the land was a base for the money supply. The government taught that the interest rate on money deposited in the government bank was closely tied to rent on an amount of government-owned land of value equal to the deposit. Well, maybe it was. I decided to dismiss from my mind this whole confusing relationship. It did not seem very important because when the government really rented out a specific piece of land, I noticed that it sought to get as much rent as it could in the marketplace, seemingly ignoring its own "average" rent figure. After all, the government officials wanted to help the government treasury in financing government projects. They always managed to explain away the difference between the rental income realized on real-life parcels they leased out and the "average" rent or interest rates they paid on bank deposits. Usually, the claim was that the particular piece of land being put up for rent was not "average."

Also, I saw that the government had an equally arbitrary and virtually unlimited authority to influence money supply by adjustment of interest rates on government bank loans and on deposits. An offer to pay high interest would bring money into the deposit pool and discourage those contemplating the seeking of loans as well. The government leaders did not do very much analysis about this. Still, if the government decided to start additional government projects, such as improving the water or sewage facilities, and needed money to pay for it, it could increase taxes or print more money to pay with, always providing the citizenry, in explanation, with some line of rationale about the action that sounded good and was politically acceptable.

These partial understandings and confusions of mine and of the typical citizen on E with regard to the backing for its currency, the money supply, and the interest rate control by the government—all were submerged when the big depression set in.

As on CONO, we start examining E's economic collapse by looking at the situation of private banks there. Again the depression was not caused by the bankers. Again, prices did not fall early and rapidly enough to compensate for the over-production and overcommitment to facilities for still more production. Again, inventories and unemployment built up quietly at first before prices could drop. Suddenly many loan clients defaulted on their loans and the banks took over assets of debtors. The market value of these assets collapsed, whether goods, land, or equipment. Those who had deposits in the private banks, as on CONO, started runs on them. The banks at the beginning were able to satisfy a demanding depositor by giving him government currency. But, as on CONO, each private bank had granted loans to a total greater than its inherent capital. It had kept some cash reserve, not lending out all of its deposits, but, with all of the depositors coming at once to get currency, the banks on E were no more able to stand up to the crisis than were the banks on CONO. They ran out of currency and could only promise to pay the depositors fully at some later date if and when they could sell assets they had obtained from their debtors or receive government currency from their remaining debtors as paybacks of loans eventually coming due.

As the depression grew, there was less money in circulation, less money on loan, and the government came into possession of more land and other assets. Of course, the government attempted to sell assets it took over at whatever the market would bring. But prices (in hard currency) were low, having collapsed with the economy. Not too many people had surplus money to buy private land, and some landowners had money problems and needed to raise money by selling, even if at a bargain price. So the price of land dropped. Land remaining in private hands brought less rent on that land from occupants in economic difficulties. The government dropped the interest rate that it would pay on deposits. Rents on housing dropped, and some housing structures went vacant while families moved in together to share rents. Farmers could sell less of their products, and they bought less seed and equipment. The island produced less, ate less, lived less well, and there was less capital invested at risk in new ventures and expansion.

The economy had indeed collapsed to a low point on E as it had on CONO. But there was no run on the government bank and no lack of confidence in the currency. No one came to the government bank with currency, representing, as it was thought, land acreage, and demanded his land. It was the law that the government would not make this exchange, but even if the government had done so, there would have been few takers. Currency on deposit would draw a little interest. In the pocket it could be used for trade. But land had to be used or rented out, neither easy to do at a gain in a depression.

E's government did not panic. It did not print more money and distribute it. How E pulled out of the economic slump we shall want to discuss very soon. For now, it is first priority to take a quick look at the island of MY where their severe depression occurred soon after. The free economy, here again, went into a downspin. But there was a new slant.

Chapter VIII

Runaway Inflation
on MY

WE RECALL that neither gold nor land was set as a base under the currency issued on MY. The money system was created in the early 1740s by an initial allocation of an amount of currency or bank deposits for each MY islander based on some habits and recollections of what a day's work or a pair of shoes should cost and a few elementary estimates of the amount of money the islanders would need to get their economy and money system started. Remember, also, that I said E's money situation, despite this peculiar beginning, sailed along fairly smoothly for years, even decades. The citizens of MY respected their currency. They were together in their commitment to trust the money supply control by the government. They paid back their loans as promised when economic conditions were favorable, not counting an infrequent exception here and there. The banks extended credit wisely, and the government taxed and spent soundly. The money supply was thus increased to keep up with the expanding population and general economic growth. If people needed to borrow money to have more to work with, they were generally successful in getting those loans if the bank had looked into the bases for repayment and found them creditable. Most of the time the bank leadership understood the market and economic growth of MY well enough to be able to assess, together with the prospective debtor, that he had a sensible plan for expansion in his activity and very probably would be able to pay back the debt—or else, no loan.

In 1750 the government, pressed by the overwhelming belief of the MY voters in the fullest of free enterprise, announced an edict that the government bank would henceforth make no loans to individuals or businesses and would limit itself to being a banker to the private banks. The latter offered interest rates on deposits and loans on a competitive, free market basis.

Before the depression occurred in the 1780s, MY had experienced several small rising and declining cycles in the economy and corresponding automatic free market adjustments and recoveries. Occasional bankruptcies and other events, embarrassing for the participants but minor in the overall economy, happened in the '50s, '60s, and '70s. Sometimes there was an oversupply of money and sometimes an undersupply, and prices fluctuated accordingly. Again, sometimes the fiscal policy of the government, its balancing of its expenditures against its income by taxes, influenced the money supply in inadvertent ways and caused some inflation or some deflation. There were short periods of substantial unemployment and product scarcities where they need not have existed. Free market, compensatory forces, along with extraordinary intervention by individuals, businesses, and banks to rescue and aid others kept these ups and downs from getting out of hand. This was true until the operations of MY had become large enough, anonymous enough, the bureaucracy big enough, the overall combination of independent actions statistical enough. Then it became possible that the adjustments to a variation, the automatic compensations, might not happen soon enough, or be strong enough. Then runaway effects could get started. When they could, they did. So MY, like E and CONO before it, suffered an economic collapse.

As I looked down on MY, with the CONO and E experience to guide me, I was no longer surprised to see the buildup of runs on the private banks. Money supply dwindled as loans collapsed and deposits collapsed with them. Those who were still liquid, although now having less income and adding up their fortunes as amounting to less, could now buy more with each MY currency dollar in goods and services. Available goods were sold for whatever they could bring in hard currency in a declining market, and people were willing to take less currency for their services in order that they might earn something to live on. Again, the problem seemed to be a failure of the prices to drop soon enough to avert the unnecessary buildup of inventories and investment in more production capacity.

The government bank at first held firm. It did not print more money and lend it to the private banks who were in need of cash to stay open. Instead, at the early stages of the panic, while it still looked like only a somewhat more severe but still temporary downturn, the government let the private banks close instead. The government bank still paid interest on any funds deposited with it and the government went on spending money for government projects. It paid with its currency. Taxes continued to be collected by the government, and payment was accepted by the government in its currency.

Of course, the private banks had to withdraw their deposits in the government bank as they tried to meet the cash demands of their depositors. However, when the first private banks to be in trouble could not repay loans to the government bank, their assets, valuable or worthless, were taken over by the government bank. The government bank's work, during this beginning period of buildup of private bank emergencies, was largely one of crossing out the entries of

deposits and loans on their records and falling heir to property of people and businesses, by way of the private banks as
funnels.

Now, at this point I began to wonder why there wasn't
more loss of confidence in the currency on MY. Why would a
fisherman accept the currency? Why would he not say, "How
do I know that this is worth anything in these troubled times,
this mere piece of paper?" Why would he not insist that he
obtain a pair of shoes if his customer were in the shoe business, or some bread from the baker or some vegetables from
the farmer or a piece of furniture to replace a broken one.
Why would not the island revert to barter, inconvenient,
clumsy, and impractical as that might seem? Why, in the
midst of all the lack of confidence, the growing unemployment, the decrease in the standard of living, did people go on
respecting the government paper as real money? Why would
not a seller rate the currency as of low value and thus
demand a great deal of it, a high price, if he were to accept
it?

After a little thought, I realized my questions could be
answered by another question. Where would the money
come from to feed such an inflationary rise in prices amidst
growing unemployment and bankruptcy? Again, checks written against deposits in a bank that could not pay in currency
no longer had much purchasing power. For payment by such
checks, the sales price in any deal rose sky-high. But anyone
paying in scarce currency could buy much more for his
dollar and new currency was not being added to the system.

Then, however, the government swung into action to
change all this. As the private banks found they could not
meet the demands of their depositors, they sought loans at
the government bank, of course. The pleas of leading banker
Emanuel Dinero were typical. He said, "Most of the loans my
bank has made are good, but I cannot expect the loans to be
paid up upon my demand tomorrow or the next day! The
businesses to whom I have lent money, almost all of them
very sound, have put that money to use. At the moment, it is

tied up in equipment and in inventory. Given just a little time, these loans will be paid back, and will fatten my supply of currency on hand. Then I shall be able to pay off every depositor who wants his money. In fact, by then he probably will not want it. A depositor wanting all his money back is obviously responding emotionally and needs only to be calmed, then things will get back to normal."

"After all," went on Dinero, "what is the role of the government bank? Now is the time the government should lend me the currency I need to meet the emergency run on my bank. When the scare is over, I shall repay the loan. You know that I have assets behind this loan, enough to cover it. It is only that those assets are all lent out at the moment."

Dinero was joined by the people at large. "Save the banks," they cried. "Print currency and lend it to every bank that is under pressure," demanded the citizenry, particularly the depositors in the banks and those with loans outstanding. "Then life will go on. We are destroying our businesses, our jobs, our economy, and our society."

It was easy for the government to decide to lend money to the private banks as a political reply to the worsening depression, and they did. In fact the government also set up some special direct loans to important individuals and big businesses in trouble—on an emergency basis only, they said— bypassing the private banks.

With the crisis developing and currency suddenly ejecting from the government bank in a fast, forceful gusher, confidence in the currency was not increased. It was decreased. Prices shot up in parallel with further diminished production activity, a drastically falling sales performance by business, a virtual moratorium on new orders being placed with factories, and rapidly growing unemployment, this despite the generosity of government loans to the private banks. It was as simple as this: the printing of a batch of currency and shipping of it to the banks who put it out to depositors seemed automatically to generate decreasing confidence and a price increase by every seller, who demanded more and more dollars for each product or service rendered and did so because he could get his price. Every business and private bank then needed even more dollars to stay alive. The government lent and printed more in turn, and prices rose further. A skyrocketing inflation soon reduced the money system to an absurdity. The money supply inflation did not save the society. Recovery had to come some other way.

Could not the government, I wondered, have shown a little restraint, printing just a bit more money, the right amount more, to go with a few carefully selected loans? Such actions, carefully controlled, might have got the economy rolling back to health. This, like some of the other questions I have left in the air, we shall take up next as we progress to a recital of how the three islands recovered, because they did.

Chapter IX

Recovery on CONO

I HAVE USED the word "panic" to describe the condition of the islands' economies in the early 1780s. I could have used that word just as well for my mental condition. For a while, I lost confidence. In everything about the islands' future? No. In the idea of a free enterprise, free market system, yes. I confess I did not know, during the peak of the difficulties on the three islands, what procedures would improve the economy. But I recovered and the islands recovered, at least to a degree. They finally took some reasoned actions, most of them sensible, I thought. And just as it took me a while to get my confidence back, some time was also required before I could understand the real nature of the problems and their efforts at solving them.

CONO had the problem first and it attacked it first. You will remember I told you that they disseminated a good part of the gold supply from the bank to the citizens as semigold coins. Perhaps it will surprise you to learn that they took all the gold back into the treasury by government decree, a little later. This was after things started to get better again, they had begun to think out the whole situation, and they decided that gold in the hands of the citizens had no substantive value in curing or averting depressions.

I had better tell you how things began to improve. For one thing, people had to eat. There was a consensus about that. The government began to buy enough food to feed anyone who could not afford to pay for it. Everyone took whatever job he could get. If a family had a few young people who had been fired and a few unemployed old ones as well, they all worked at whatever pay they were offered. The government increased its expenditures on government projects. Many worked for the government, assigning food supplies and doing other tasks it was decided should be mounted, such as improving roads, dams, harbors, and government buildings. As they began to eat better, even though less well than before, and started to receive paychecks again (which they had to spend rather quickly—savings were certainly down), money began to turn over. That is when I truly appreciated that economic activity was related not only to the money supply but to the velocity of its motion from hand to hand.

It became apparent gradually that there was a real demand for more output from the farms and the factories, and employment rose. Everyone realized they had previously provided an overcapacity for many products, so there was little factory expansion for a good while, but an increasing use of available capacity. Some folks acquired a bit more money than they could use immediately and decided finally to take the risk of putting that money in the bank even though the interest rates were awfully low. The banks that opened their doors kept more of the deposits in reserve and granted fewer loans than before. The excess currency in circulation, that had led to inflationary prices, began to represent less of an excess as production increased to meet the demand and prices began to come down.

Part of the recovery, I guess I am trying to say, was

natural. If the government had not gone overboard in increasing the currency supply, the recovery might have come earlier, and even more naturally. CONO would have been spared the episode of an inflation following the initial deflation of currency values. The deflation was an inherent part of the original economic slump. The subsequent inflation was the result of unwise governmental overreaction.

A lot of government regulations were passed in 1782. Almost all intelligent men, and many of the others, were trying to figure out how to avert a future major depression. Everyone running for office had ideas, some good, some bad, some that he could sell, and some that were laughed at. There were suggestions, for instance, for eliminating money and substituting some sort of scrip based on hours worked, which almost all of the voters realized immediately was just another name for money except for implied rules concerning acquiring and using it that were not clear and perhaps dangerous. But some proposals proved popular and were immediately approved and implemented, because everyone was for decisive action.

For example, they decided to restrict private banking greatly and have the government insure a part of the deposits in private banks. As I saw this happening, I prayed they not go too far. After all, you cannot stop people from borrowing from one another with the lenders expecting more money in return. How practical was it for the government to step in and make rules? I had to admit that when private banks get big and suck in a lot of the public's money, a potential danger exists that they may lend too much of it out without sufficient judgment and end up hurting the whole country. Of course, any banker that operated this way would soon go out of business. In a free economy, who would deposit his funds in a bank with a poor reputation for liquidity and loan policy? However, the government said, "Why should a bank's leadership, unmonitored by the island's elected representatives, have hands on the throttle of the economy?"

What did the new controls turn out to be? They included insisting that a bank have a large amount of true net worth—that is, funds belonging entirely to the owners of the bank—before they were licensed to operate as a bank, as compared with past practice. Furthermore, each private bank was required to deposit a substantial fraction of this internal worth, its real, completely owned capital, in the government bank. Also required was that private banks be examined by government auditors regularly and that their assets, deposits, and loan totals be made public, and thus subject to scrutiny. The private banks also were to meet some stiff criteria as to their loan policies, the most important of which was that they could lend out in total only a portion of all the money deposited with them and, more particularly, a smaller fraction than had been the history of the immediate past. The government, in other words, took upon itself the close regulation of private banks and the ensuring of conservative, safe policies. It was understood by everyone that the government would control in such a way as to curb the extent to which the banks could gamble on economic growth. "No more will private banks expand the money supply almost at their will!" said Fidel Geronimo, the leading government advocate of severe banking regulations.

Of course, I felt that bankers could not expand the money supply recklessly or their banking business would soon be in some more prudent banker's hands. I worried more that entrepreneurs on CONO, wanting to enlarge their operations, and companies or individuals seeking to borrow money, would find it somewhat more difficult to raise funds. With the government setting up impediments to sensible credit action, would this not inhibit economic growth on CONO, a treasured ambition of mine? But they did very little thinking then about the impact of these regulations on future expansion. They were busy worrying about preventing future disastrous depressions.

Earlier, I said CONO called all the gold back in from its citizens. Let us see what that was all about. Their offering of gold in exchange for currency seemed to have a pronounced, beneficial effect at the time. Insecurity about their economic futures in 1782 was far less than it had been a year before. The gold, when sitting in a box in the central bank (they talked about it often as "CONO's gold" and that gave me a warm feeling) was their security blanket. Most people in a few months voluntarily had deposited right back in the bank almost all the gold they had obtained. It really didn't prove convenient to keep the gold at home, except perhaps to have a sample to look at occasionally, and interest was not being earned on that money.

Besides, do not forget that the government had changed the price of the gold from the historical value they had all learned about and still retained in the backs of their minds. Gold had been the sacred money base. They used to think of a dollar bill as being worth a particular amount of gold, and now that same dollar was worth a tenth of that amount. What is more, it was demonstrated that this ratio was and always could be determined again by government edict. Almost the simplest of men could see that the government had it in its power to change the value of the currency in terms of gold at will. So, was gold so special? What they all wanted was to get on with their work and have secure jobs, return to eating regularly, see a future for their young, the currency stable, the banks solid.

I listened in on conversations amongst the more intelligent people. I remember hearing one discussion in which a rather bright young man, Frederico Miltones, said, "What if we had enough gold on the island so that everyone could have an enormous amount of it? Would we all then be rich? Could we all stop working? If so, what would be produced? Nothing! We would have nothing to buy and yet all that gold to buy it with! What does wealth really consist of? We want to satisfy our needs and then, on top of that, to possess some luxuries to enjoy. Thus, it is vital that we work and produce what we need and want. If gold can be exchanged for goods, it is valuable. But the amount of gold that sits in the bank and that is said to be behind our currency is arbitrary."

His views were echoed by others. "Miltones is right. If the whole island has only a little gold, then gold is prized, and each ounce is worth many dollars. If there is an abundance of gold, then gold is cheap and we price it at far fewer dollars per ounce. If we could find it easily almost everywhere, we would not even bother to pick it all out of the ground. If we could discover none, the government could just as well pretend it had come upon a secret source, and that its box was full. Then it could print up paper money to represent the gold, just as it has indeed done, so that we would have currency to use. What is important is to keep the money printing under control and produce goods and food." This became the popular view.

But how to control the money supply?

I mentioned that they decided to regulate the private banks. They also set up strict rules for the government bank. They appointed a special permanent commission whose job it would be to decide on the amount of money that should be in circulation. If the government bank prints up and lends out money too freely, they argued, this could cause an oversupply of money. This act would be certain a little later to inflate the price of everything. But worse than this, it would distort the economy. With easy credit, everyone would be invited to gamble on developing a larger business, to live higher, spend more, and count on bigger returns than he would be bound to get. Employment saturation would occur and the price of labor would increase dramatically as business sought more workers than were available. Then prices would rise and so would interest rates, because anyone lending money would expect the real value of the dollar to be far less when, later, the loan was repaid.

Of course, the rising prices and interest rates, they knew, represented good, automatic compensation by the free market. The same would be true of the overproduction, if it occurred due to easy credit. Overexpansion would eventually create too big a supply for the demand, causing the prices to fall back again. Still, misjudgments in the direction of overexpansion would be almost certain and, if severe, widespread, and sudden enough, seeds for a depression might be started. An explosive trend might develop that could not be corrected soon enough by the free market's automatic reversing forces. Once started, the inevitable rapid downward cycle, a collapse, would follow the unjustified ballooning of the economy, and the horrible experience of 1780 would be repeated.

The commission was instructed to expect, wait for, and count on relying upon natural corrections. For instance, small overexpansion in one area should not be of concern. Soon many of those products would go unsold and their prices would fall. That would be enough to discourage further overexpansion. The federal commission should not overreact. It should not respond to such trivial little scares. It should expect some minor oscillations, and it should expect timely and adequate, if not immediate and full, compensatory adjustments to occur without governmental intervention.

It should seek to work out, however, that rate of increase in money supply that would be stable. The rise in money in deposits and out in circulation should match properly with increases in population, production, and the productivity of workers and with the overall sound economic growth of the island. There should be money available to invest in legitimate technological advance that could increase the ability of the average worker to produce. Money should be sufficient for growth to keep people generally employed and supplied.

The critical way to judge whether the money supply is expanding too much is by noting whether it is expanding at a faster rate than output. There has to be too much money chasing too few goods before there is inflation. If we can increase productivity and employment, thus producing more, then we must see to it that the money supply rises in proper proportion to keep prices stable. This assumes that the velocity of money remains about the same.

It was also seen that there should not be an expectancy of zero unemployment. First of all, they reasoned, flexibility existed in what is meant by "unemployment." How young a child, for example, should be expected to bring earnings into the family, and how old or infirm an adult? What about working mothers? What about the amount of work a young person might be expected to perform while still studying for his profession? The problem would always be present of some excess workers in a field of activity that had overexpanded. They would be out of work temporarily while relocating or retraining for some other activity that needed expansion.

It would be well to recognize that full employment was probably an unattainable ideal and even a handicap because no inventory of available workers would exist to provide for flexibility in economic growth. The trick was to keep unemployment down to a level that could be tolerated, they reasoned. This level should be one where unemployed persons could get a reasonable amount of financial help so that they and their families would not starve. Perhaps the government ought to see to this. Government action would be like an insurance policy, every citizen paying to create a reserve in the government treasury that could be used to pay out a minimum income to those who were temporarily in need.

So CONO, through a combination of what I have called natural forces and well-thought-out government actions and regulations, began to restore the economy. People went back to work. By 1783, further expansion began on CONO.

It was about at this time that I finally concluded I had been wrong about some of my fundamental thinking when I started the entire project that led to the populating of the three islands. Was I fooled about the benefits of free enterprise and a free market? No. Could a free market be free of instabilities? No. Of that I was certain. There would be ups and downs always, fluctuations of supply and demand, the impact of new discoveries, the effect of failures of judgment, too much risk, entrepreneurs getting over their heads in business, people living too high for their incomes. Economic growth could not be smooth. But the big issue I had yet to reason out in the 1780s was whether sooner or later instabilities need build to a runaway effect—that is, unless there are very strict governmental rules and controls. Maybe a depression could occur, even if that regulation existed, perhaps for reasons that would eventually develop and that I had not yet been able to foresee and comprehend, just as I was unable to see ahead to the 1780 depression.

The citizens must band together to some degree, that is, through their government. Careful setting of rules, patrolling of the free market's operations to avert economic cycles so extreme they are disastrous to the economy and to the people—these are necessary duties for government. But now we come to the question: How severe and how broad and how strict must the rules be? May we permit only a little bit of free enterprise, or may it be almost entirely free with everyone almost able to do as he chooses, with only a modest amount of policing by government?

I did not have to ponder these matters by isolated thought, because the three islands below were engaged in fighting the problem and working out, each in its own way, their experimental attempts to answer these questions. More accurately, I would say they worked out something approaching stability. They used various hybrid mixtures of a free enterprise society and a government-controlled one. But I still did not know whether any of them had done it in the best way. Did any invent the least controls, the closest approach to a true free market with minimum government intervention? It was not clear to me that the more government controls, the more stability. Even accepting, for the moment, the evils of government domination, such as loss of individual initiative by the citizens, dependence on the government rather than on their own efforts and foresight, the loss of risk-taking and hence the failure to take bold, original steps—does government involvement guarantee no depression?

Surely, the value of government control must hinge on what kind of controls and how administered. It is, in other words, a matter of quality, not quantity of control. Perhaps a little control of just the right kind can go a long way and, if so, it safeguards the essence of free enterprise. At the same time that it does this, it provides ample insurance against a runaway condition. One can imagine, at least, very severe controls over many aspects of the society, with chaotic instability still developing, because something important has gone unnoticed and uncontrolled. But why theorize? What really happened on the islands?

Chapter X

The Controlled Economy of E

E BROUGHT ITS ECONOMY under control after its depression by a most complete and strict governmental domination over the economy. Even after another hundred years, it did not overcome the tendency toward government regulation left from its first reaction to a major economic collapse.

E slapped tight rules on the money supply. As with CONO, E did not blame the depression on the banks. Yet the government set up rigid measures on the operations of banks. It specified interest rates for all loans and deposits, leaving no room for corrections or influence on these rates by free market forces. Whether governmentally or privately owned, the government set all rental fees on land. The government recognized the effects of increasing population on the demand for and the value of land by increasing rents regularly in some proper proportion, it thought, to general growth. It controlled not only the printing of money in close relationship to its evaluation of the economy's needs but, of course, it did the same with credit. These controls went, we see, far beyond the actions on CONO.

Periodically the government published the official figures on the actual money supply, the sum of currency in circulation and deposits in the banks, and it worried and acted somehow if the deviation from plan was pronounced. It sought to make certain that there would be no inflation to speak of, and no significant deflation, by setting prices on most services and commodities. If a fluctuating supply to demand relationship made it too difficult to hold prices firm, the government provided tax and other inducements to increase supply, or took actions to cut demand by sponsoring substitutes, or provided subsidies to suppliers if they would agree to manipulate capacity and supply.

There was a law fixing both minimum and maximum wages, altered from time to time. As more inventions increased productivity and enabled the food growers and the fishermen to produce more food per hour of effort, the rules held the fishermen's and the food growers' wages constant and decreased prices so people could buy more to eat. As the population increased, and, along with it, the money supply and the pace of business, E's government broadened its own programs and expenditures, taxing in accordance with income and receiving a greater total for the government to spend as the economy expanded.

Ask a typical family head and worker on the island of E in the year 1800 how much money he had and what he could buy with it and his answer would show he was much better off than his father had been twenty-five years before in 1775. He had more money in the bank, a better house, enjoyed more luxuries, ate from a larger variety of foods, had more clothes, a superior education, better communications, and possessed more gadgets to make his life productive, interesting, and pleasant. Was this because of the strong controls that had been in force for two decades or despite them? I was very interested in trying to get the answer to that question.

There was more, as I shall soon describe, to the extent of government domination of the economy on the island of E, and I cannot say they put these controls into effect and applied them so earnestly solely because they had reasoned out that only by doing so could they avoid a future catastrophic economic turndown. It was rather apparent to me that they simply had got into the habit. They initially had perceived a need for government action to restore the economy and inspire confidence after they had endured the depression for enough time. Somehow, however, it seemed they went even further and developed a permanent dependency on excess governmental control.

Perhaps the concept of tight direction by government stemmed from the personalities of the leaders in the 1780s who became enamored of the possibilities of using governmental control as a formula for economic health. They did so, I must say, in all sincerity, not out of personal ambition, least of all villainy. They wished for their nation a more secure life—one that they thought could be maximized as to economic growth and would provide the most for the citizens. The government leaders surrounded themselves with the most brilliant of the island's young thinkers who were happy to become involved with the source of power, motivated by nothing but a heartfelt desire to see that every person and physical asset would be usefully employed to the fullest and that more goods would be produced and distributed. They convinced themselves it would be better for all of the island's population if those with the best understanding were to plan for everyone else.

Their planning went beyond the control of wages, money supply, interest rates, rents, and prices. The elite group of planners watched the economy constantly to detect any tendency toward an instability. If they observed some unemployment, for example, they quickly started a government project or a retraining program or made it easier for some industries to borrow money to expand in an effort to nip the growing unemployment in the bud. Admittedly, as they saw new products being developed on which there were as yet no price controls, they waited a while. But the moment it appeared the producers of those new products might make a rather high profit because of an excessive demand compared with the supply, then they immediately applied their price control. If it seemed there was a shortage of housing compared with the need—I thought because of insufficient profit, and hence too little incentive, for those who provided houses —they decreased interest rates for mortgages on homes and for loans to builders who thus were encouraged to borrow working capital for construction.

I began to realize that on the island of E this was no longer an emergency, stopgap campaign to cure the depression and prevent future ones. This was becoming the way of life, a thoroughly government-controlled economy. "Is free enterprise on E totally dead?" I asked myself. No, it was not. It was still possible for individuals to start businesses if they already had the money or could get credit. It was still possible to get slightly rich, to use ingenuity, to be motivated to put capital to work if one possessed it, or ideas if one had those. But it was a lot harder.

If something novel was conceived, one had only a short time in which to realize the maximum profit of a venture to exploit the innovation before the government would step in to control profits. If a man performed better than his competitor, he might find the government stepping in to alter the rules of the game. It never did that in his losing competitor's favor, exactly; the government always tried, usually even appeared, to be fair to all. But rather than having a chance at putting one's inferior performance competitors to shame and taking over more of the entire market (and then, as a result, being able to realize greater profits) one could expect the government to ease up on credit for all. This would help the poor competitors who otherwise would have been desperate for funds for their ailing businesses, while helping the successful one not very much at all, because he hardly needed the credit boost. Or again, if unemployment began to develop with the poorly performing business as its sales volume dropped and that of the successful firm built up, the government might increase taxes to cover unemployment relief.

These taxes would be paid largely, of course, by the successful, profit-making entrepreneur. With the tax revenue used
to pay the unemployed, they would not be expected to come
begging for a lower-paying job enabling the cutting of labor
costs. Besides, the government laws kept wages constant.

To the capitalist and employer, the government on E
seemed to be prolabor, always holding wages up, when they
should be dropping at times to allow free market adjustment
to take place. To labor leaders, who worked to better the lot
of the worker, the government seemed to be probusiness,
always holding wages down, when they should be rising.

Few of the benefits of automatic free-market, free-
enterprise adjustments were realized on E. Little motivation
existed for putting private capital at great risk. Little of significance happened to the economy of E, or to the society in
general, without government participation.

Each year the government of E put aside some of the tax
money into a reserve. Then, when it appeared that the
economy was advancing too slowly, the unemployment rate
threatening to be a bit higher than it was felt it needed to be,
government projects would be started. Programs would be
launched to improve the water supply or sewage systems, for
example, or the roads or means for communicating up and
down the island. They would make improvements in the
schools and the hospitals which were, of course, government-
furnished facilities on the island of E. Once, when unemployment threatened amongst scientists and engineers, E started a
project to study how to conquer the ocean, a program specifically aimed at landing a man in California and returning him
alive, which though called a boondoggle by many, kept the
technical professionals active. It yielded valuable "fallout"
ideas, according to the program's advocates, although no dis-
cernible progress in crossing the ocean.

For me it was fascinating to watch the continual contest
between the government's directors of the economy and the
incorrigible actions of the free market. Thus, I remember
one period in 1795 when a sudden and mysterious disease

killed a large fraction of the pigs on the island. For months there were few jobs for those who raised pigs, prepared them for market, cut them up and sold them, whether for food or for their hides. Unemployment began to soar in all related industries, such as leather clothing items and shoes. The supply was low compared with the demand, of course, and demand increased for substitute products for food and clothing.

E's government commanders did what I had learned they could be expected to do. They noted the situation developing, anticipated some of the repercussions, and commenced to take action early. They started government work projects, for example. Only a fraction of those who were thrown out of work in the pursuits related to the raising, selling, and utilization of pigs and their remains could find work directly on these government projects. But the projects tended to pull labor from all over the island in various other activities, leaving shortages. As the shortages became evident here and there, the government started training programs to fill the new jobs with the newly unemployed who did not have the specific skills needed. Meanwhile, they paid the unemployed a reasonable wage so they could all eat and not disturb the society by their poverty or the economy by their lack of purchasing ability.

Where the government's economic tsars, despite their brilliance and powers, had difficulty, however, was in the control of prices and wages. A pig grower going to work in an unfamiliar activity was less useful to his employer, of course, even though the employer had to pay him by law the same, or nearly the same, wages as a more experienced worker. Several specialists in the treating of hides transferred to fabrication of cotton garments. Their poor productivity, because of their lack of expertise, increased the cost of producing the cotton goods. But since the government had fixed the prices, despite the increasing demand for cotton products, even for quickly invented cotton cord and bamboo sandals to replace leather shoes, the cotton manufacturer showed poorer profits.

Of course, the manager of the cotton company innovated and maneuvered to the maximum extent possible within the law. For example, he sought to produce and sell as many as possible of his cotton-bamboo sandals at a maximum price during the temporary shortage of pigskin shoes before the government put a price ceiling on his completely new product. Or, in providing his data to the Price Board so they could set the ceiling price on his product as required by law, he naturally used the records of the performances of his workers in the early stages of the manufacturing of the product when they were still learning and hence slow. He hoped that a high price would be established based on these high initial costs. He might then be able to bring his costs down, as the employees got the hang of making the new product, and his profits would rise.

With the stoppage of production of leather shoes, a great demand sprang up for the available leather shoes still on the shelves. The retail stores whose inventories contained a substantial quantity of unsold shoes—perhaps because their appearance and fit were poor or the retailer had simply misjudged the size of his market earlier and ordered too many—could now sell off these "lemons." Instead of the annual bargain sale during which he would reduce prices and accept a lower profit (which would be par for the course on some of his merchandise at times during the year) the retailer was now able to sell anything in leather at the maximum price allowed by law. Thus, people found that their costs had risen to keep shoes on their feet despite price control.

I could cite you a hundred other examples. The government could not defeat supply and demand with price and wage controls. For short times they could distort people's freedom of choice, their free market, whether as consumers or job seekers, by controls and thus obtain the appearance of fixed wages and prices. But the moment I looked beneath the surface I saw free choice and supply and demand always making a comeback.

So, I don't want to give the impression that E's was a thoroughly docile population, completely accepting the wage, price, rent, and other controls. The government's programs, budgets, taxation to raise the funds for expenditures, and its control of banking and credit and the issuance of money seemed to be solidly supported, however. Less so, wage and price controls. Every few years there would be a popular wave of demand for reforms of government controls. Politicians running for office would promise improvements, less or more controls, and they could manipulate the otherwise strong and independent body of government economists by new appointments when elected.

One of the big issues on E in 1805 was whether there should be pay increases with time as a man grew older. One Senilio Iquerias said that there was inadequate recognition of the value of experience. He had correctly guessed that his rhetoric on behalf of the older citizens would appeal to more than half of the voters, having carefully arranged his arguments to define "experienced" as encompassing the age group of more than half of the voting population. To these workers he promised increases in salaries.

After election, Iquerias's majority constituency expected to live better after receiving wage boosts. The economic council that had the power to adjust wages and prices refused to go along at first. However, the pressure of public opinion was tremendous. Also important were some of the things that the political leadership could do to influence the economy independent of the wage and price control board (like holding up important projects that should be accomplished and which, if held back, could disrupt the economy more than the small increase in wages) that a wage increase greater than what was considered by the economic council to be justified was finally approved.

Of course, the effect was to disturb the economy. The combination of prices remaining fixed and wages higher meant that there was less profit in producing anything. This meant it was not attractive for many businesses and industries to provide some specific products and services, since the return on their investment was now too poor. Thus, they began to dismiss some of the "older" employees and the government had to step up its government projects and training programs and unemployment relief. The businesses that were producing less profit also paid less taxes. The government had to dip into the reserves it had been piling up, presumably, for just such situations. There was a collapse of supply in many areas on which the prices were fixed with such severity. Substitute goods at higher prices began to show up on the market, keeping the economic council busy trying to assess these and slap price controls on them as they appeared. In effect, prices were going up because people had to fill their needs with these substitute items. More people had to be employed by the government to work out all of these things, so there were fewer people left to produce the goods. The older people were put back to work either in the government or doing something in business producing new products which, of necessity, were more expensive to produce, these new products being poor substitutes for products that could have been produced for less if there had not been the disturbance.

The government then countered by passing some rules prohibiting the firing of older employees. This raised costs more, hurt profits, and distorted production further into higher priced substitutes. For all practical purposes, people had less, worked less efficiently, and lived less well. The island was really producing less that was useful and valuable to the citizens and was engaged more in bureaucratic follow-up, conniving, and assessing. As the bulletins were issued weekly on prices for everything and wages were held fixed, everyone had difficulty finding the products for sale that he really wanted. To get a good pair of shoes, hidden in the back room, now that the older people who knew how to make them well were doing something else, almost required doing a favor for the shoemaker—for example, giving him priority over other customers when he, in turn, wanted to buy something. In effect, there was a black market in which one could buy what he wanted but only by doing something that would not be noted and counted by the government.

There were many other specific pieces of foolishness—I had a large list for E and its insistent government controls by the year 1800 and more as the new century's years changed to decades. It was 1810 when Eduardo de la Cantata invented a foot-operated machine for sewing that cut the cost of most assemblies of cloth to one half, assuming the sewers received the same wages, which the government made a requirement. Of course, clothes became cheaper, people could buy more for the same budgeted outlay, and the factories, to meet the new higher demand, increased production.

However, the total amount spent for clothes did not increase—people apparently were satisfied to obtain more garments that first year for the same money. So the factories received no higher gross sales dollars. The government set a lower price ceiling on the new clothes made more cheaply. Everybody, however, underestimated the high cost to the factories of installing the machines and maintaining them. Unfortunately, all concerned were optimistic, machine designers and makers, their purchasers, the clothing manufacturers, alike. The machines began to malfunction and wear out. The result? Clothing manufacturers, having paid for the machines, sustained additional costs and lost money. They cut their production way down and let many employees go. Some manufacturers went back to hand sewing again and received government approval for higher prices. Others were stuck with the low machine-made price structure that was below their costs and ended up in real financial difficulties. It was all straightened out eventually. But meanwhile, though the nation had discovered a better way of providing a necessity, it lost time and money, and the economy and society were hurt rather than benefited, because of the confusion generated by E's fixation on pervasive government control and involvement.

The most persistent and stubborn government impact

on the economy of E, and at the same time the least successful, was this attempt to control the price of every conceivable
little product and service. Again and again the government,
in its price-fixing mania, would be outmaneuvered by free
market forces but would always fight back. If it was not the
cumbersomeness and complexity of the system, and the lack
of adequate and timely information, it was human cussed-
ness, unanticipated entries of new ideas, and changes in
product and service availability and consumer acceptance
that thwarted the government in its ambition for total price
control. A host of human errors figured in as did black
marketeering, or its equivalent, favoritism in contracting and
purchasing arrangements between friends or between clever
people who knew how to find loopholes in the supposedly
fixed price structure.

But I must say that E's government gradually learned
how, over the years, to hold prices in line to the maximum
extent possible. Part of it, of course, was not all that difficult.
The government could be expected to be successful in exerting tight control over the price to be paid for services which
the government provided, such as water supply and waste
removal. Even for some products put out by private industry,
the prices could be said to be administered rather than free
market ones because the product turned out to be provided
by essentially a monopoly. For example, on E a company
founded by one Maximilian Tercito provided all of the
paper. There had been early competitors but they had been
forced out of business owing to the exceptional performance
of Tercito and his five sons after him in the technology of
extracting the necessary key ingredients out of existing island
vegetation and in organizing efficient systems for acquiring
and processing the materials and distributing the finished
product.

There was a given need for paper and the monopoly
company was privileged to decide on the price. (I do not want
to suggest that the Tercito company, in the absence of any
price controls, could necessarily have upped its prices a great

deal. If it had raised the price of paper too high, it would undoubtedly have forced the islanders out of the habit of using paper.) With a single company in control of a product area the government could more easily see how costs, profit and prices relate, even though the product might change from time to time. The expenses of running the paper business included paying for water and rent on government leased land. In both the government was much in control. There was also interest expense on borrowed money used by the paper company with the rate set by the government. Finally, the wages were under government control, whether for the gatherers of the raw material, the processing of it or the final distribution of the paper product. It was thus about as straightforward for the government to administer prices on paper as on the dissemination of mail or water.

The big problem for the government in price control was in those areas where free market forces were actively at work. However, it was not only in the pricing arena where the government's insistent desire to direct the economy came up against annoying, uncontrollable forces that kept mixing in. Take, for example, the matter of control of interest rates and credit. It is one thing to set interest rates for government banks but another thing to try to do it for borrowings between individuals, and between small businesses. Two little companies whose managements were friendly could arrange to do some shifting of money between them. A supplier, for example, would agree to postpone a required payment from his customer with the understanding that he would receive more payment later, this arrangement really amounting to a loan from one company to the other and a payment of interest. The government fought to get into the act of all conceivable deals that could be the equivalent of extending credit and paying of interest. Always, however, another bypass could be added to the deal by scheming dealers continually thwarting the government's attempted control while staying just on the good side of the legal limit to freedom of action.

Actually, for a while E tried to set up bans against any private lending between individuals and companies. No one, they said, is allowed to be in debt to anyone else with the exception of banks. But this turned out to be unenforceable and, while they maintained the rule on the books and by doing so discouraged informal lending, a certain amount of it nevertheless went on. How could the grocer refuse a loaf of bread to a good customer who was out of change but would pay off, he knew, the next day?

E's government particularly had problems with rent control on housing. E's leadership always claimed that the real purpose of rent control was not alone to help ensure a stable economy, one with no large inflationary or deflationary excursions. It was also to arrange that islanders financially less well off could still get reasonably good housing at low prices. This meant that the government was inclined to set rents at a low value as a political ploy.

At one point in 1815, they directed a sudden lowering of rents on about a quarter of all of the housing on the island. The demand for housing thus increased, since more people were now able to afford the housing. Many lower income families who had been living together or in small quarters decided they could now afford to spread out. But there was no sudden increase in the supply of houses to rent to meet the higher demand. For every vacant house, there were several families ready to pay the new low rental fee and move in. So who got the housing space? The openings were filled, obviously, but it was not by free market competition. Somehow, a form of rationing had to be devised.

The allocation was done first by the landlords themselves who, now that they could ask no more than the government-fixed rent, looked for tenants desirable in other ways—for example, good looks or no children, or offers of what amounted to a bribe, such as the willingness to buy some deteriorating furniture in the dwelling at an outrageous price. Of course, the government attempted to fix the price of used furniture, but that was quite difficult. How broken-down may a chair be and still be counted as a chair?

My analysis, as I looked down at the impact of E's tight rental controls, was that it helped the rich more than the poor. Rent controls simply kept the latter in the housing available, which began to deteriorate quickly. The rents were too low, in the opinion of the owners of the housing, to allow them to maintain them properly and still obtain a good return on investment. Those with little means, who lived in this bad housing at the fixed rents, would have been better off to pay a bit more, stimulating the production of more and better housing, or at least, the repair of the housing in which they were living. The lower paid worker was denied by the government the privilege of using such money as he had—that is, all of his competitive powers, including price competition—to buy the most satisfactory housing on a free market.

A similar situation applied to the setting of a minimum wage scale by the government. This tended to keep the young, inexperienced workers or the very old or stupid, slow ones from being employed at all and forced them into only occasional and unsatisfactory work, or idleness, and a poor income. Meanwhile, to keep them from starving, the state supplied an additional token income to these marginal workers at the expense of the real workers who were paying taxes to provide these government funds for unemployment relief. A business that might have employed a few such low-contribution workers at less than the minimum wage now found that it just did not pay to keep them on the payroll. It was better to produce less than to try to produce more with these unsatisfactory workers; their contribution to income of the business was less than the amount paid them in wages and in costs for supporting equipment and material.

Dadel Vizo, an engineer on E in the early 1800s, made an excellent living as an efficiency consultant, based on this minimum wage law. He had the reputation of being able to study any industrial operation and show how, by the use of some added tools and new methods, some of the less productive workers could be eliminated and the production increased, the expense of the purchase of the new equipment and the pay for Vizo's services being less than the cost of the labor dismissed from the job. I am sorry that other matters caused me to lose track of how Vizo fared. When I last checked, about in 1820, the government attempted to fix his wages, and he had outflanked the government by working out a commission to be paid him as a percentage of savings to the company client, in lieu of wages. I suspect the government finally caught up with him and managed to make his work less profitable to him, demotivating him in the process and depriving industry on E of the steady contribution that he otherwise would have continued to make to the improving productivity on the island.

Of course, occasionally these indecencies, born of too much governmental interference in the economy, which I could see so readily from above, began to be noticed by the citizens below. Partial inhibitions on such extensive government tampering with every operation of the economy would be considered and even implemented, here and there. But government control on E had become human nature, and the young and old alike took it for granted that it should be so.

From my vantage point, I could compare what was happening on the island of E with, say, the island of CONO. I could see that E was making less progress by some of my personal standards. I would have been frustrated in realizing my ambitions had I been down on E alive and striving for advancement, as I would have defined it. With prices and wages fixed, with the continual struggle between government domination and free enterprise, little incentive for growth existed.

The government of E wanted a controlled economy to prevent depressions and guarantee stable economic growth. This led them to wage and price and other controls but it also led them to judge their success by whether or not there was noticeable unemployment. Unemployment, they felt, was basically unforgivable. It was antisocial because people wanted to work and should be able to find work and because it was unfair for hard-working citizens to have to support those who contributed nothing. Besides, unemployed citizens

did not aid in attaining the economic growth which they
wanted. But by trying to be certain that everyone would be
employed, the government had to mix into business and
industry planning and interfere with the free market even
more.

The moment some industry's products were less in demand and some layoffs occurred, the government became
nervous and tried either to get that industry to expand or
make their products more acceptable. Failing this, they
sought to subsidize it, to share its costs, get it reorganized, or
something. But this was not always a good idea. Sometimes
lagging industries simply should have been allowed to
contract.

The smaller the unemployment, the more difficult it was
to reduce it. But the government oftentimes matched this
increasing difficulty with a more and more intense effort, to
little avail.

There was even too little motivation for doing a job
well. By 1820, the range of wage differences allowed to
compensate good workers as against mediocre producers had
become almost nil. Indeed, wherever it became temporarily
noticeable it was because there were occasions in which
worker shortages developed in some product and the producer, seeking a quick response, connived ways to attract the
needed workers with the equivalent of additional pay on the
side. Phillipe Susa, a metals manufacturer, and a leading
amateur musician and singer of great repute over the entire
island, was able to obtain better workers at the same government-fixed salary by promising free concerts and lessons
(under the guise of merely inviting his workers to his exclusive amateur musicales). That his wife was shapely and given
to dancing at these concerts with much originality and little
attire also gave these free concerts a special value to the
workers which the government could not easily interpret as a
violation of the fixed salary regulations.

With total determination to have wage and price controls, E's government found it was continually forced to

control more and more of the economy. Government con-
trollers would meet with setbacks, finding control to be
elusive, even realizing that their attempts might be harming
the economic growth which they also sought. Yet, dropping
some attempts, starting new ones, they held to and developed
the habit. Control was assumed as right, and lack of it
construed as failure. They accepted the fact that they could
not have a perfect score, that some failure was inevitable, but
they didn't like it and they kept on trying.

An example of this escalation of control is found by
looking at the matter of assignment of labor resources. In
some industries, as product acceptance fell off through one or
another change in the economy, technological development,
or social patterns, a free market would have led to a dismissal
of workers and a lowering of the wage rate in that industry,
for a time at least—natural corrective forces. A young boy's
father might tell him to shift from helping the fisherman at a
modest pay to working for a housebuilder. The father might
guess this to be better because he detected an increasing
demand for housing. The people on E had the privilege of
exerting their free will to some extent to take new jobs and
abandon old ones. Now, if too many sons exerted such a free
right to move about in accordance with their fathers' estimates of what would happen to the economy, they could
obviously affect the supply of workers in industries which the
government was meanwhile trying to control as the father to
all. It was natural for government planners to become upset
if some needed product manufacturer did not have enough
workers, for if the production was too low compared with the
demand, the free market might force the prices up somehow.
The government observers would then have had to expend
more effort to watch and control to meet their objective of
fixed prices.

A consequence was the inevitable decision by the government that workers should be forced to stay at their jobs.
So, to wage and price controls, we then add job control, job
assignments by government—a government draft, so to speak.

But job control when tried on E, partway, would never work out. It would become a little war between the government and the people. The contest would either be won by the workers or, if won by the government, would be sabotaged by poor motivation and poor productivity. Thus, the idea of job assignment by E's government would come and go. There was always a little of it. It was always on its way out in one small aspect of the island's activities and on its way in somewhere else, sometimes being labeled as an emergency condition with special rewards for cooperation and sometimes coming in under another name. Specially improved working conditions would be used to attract workers in an area of short labor supply rather than to force them to take the jobs, but this still constituted government interference in what would otherwise have been a free market for workers.

A man who could turn out a pair of shoes in a day, noticing that his fellow workers took two days, could see no reason for hurrying. He dillydallied, talked and joked more than necessary, and still drew the same average pay. His less capable associates, seeing the best man taking it easy, were encouraged to do the same. Both quality and quantity in producing shoes suffered. There could have been more, better, and cheaper shoes or there could have been fewer people engaged in making them, had there not been so much government control of the machinery.

Of course, there were exceptions, still speaking of shoes. There was the skillful worker Larello, who, able to complete his shoes with high quality very quickly, commenced to make fancier and more complex shoes. These the owner of the factory, Olivera, was able to take to the government and get reclassified as higher priced shoes, not only because they were fancy but because it was believable that they cost more to make. The new styles turned out to be desired by the wealthier people of the island, so the production was profitable. The skillful employee, Larello, had been instrumental in expanding the shoe factory's products and its profits. Olivera was pleased and would have liked to have offered

Larello a bonus. He was not able to raise Larello's pay very much. That would have violated the government rule. However, after such incidents were repeated many times, Olivera gave Larello a share of the factory. This was allowed by law (although a gift tax had to be paid because the government was not about to encourage employers to cheat on the fixed wage rules by bonuses and gifts) .

As a minority partner of the shoe firm, our enterprising and artistic worker soon stopped fabricating shoes and worked exclusively at designing them. A little later, Larello started a factory of his own and became a key competitor to the original factory where he got his start. He was able to obtain credit at the bank because of his strong record and went on to other activities. Later he was honored as a high contributor to the economic growth, wealth, and standard of living of the island.

While this kind of thing occurred frequently on CONO, it was relatively rare on the island of E. The citizens on E were more secure in that they were confident of steady incomes and steady jobs. They did not know there was a better life to be attained by relaxing on government controls. They were accustomed to tight rule by government. They depended on it. The government leadership and the voting citizens together sincerely believed that they had found the formula. Theirs, they thought, was a very good match between the required role of the government to maintain a safe and secure economy without dangerous instabilities, on the one hand, and free enterprise, on the other. They did not realize they were not allowed the freedom really to engage in activities of their choice, to use their ingenuity fully, and to invest their personal wealth at risk according only to their own judgments and abilities.

It was understandable, perhaps, for me to make the error of believing that, because I had selected my original colonists with care and subjected them to my lectures, all were totally sold on free enterprise as the route to the good life. It was somewhat less forgivable of me to apply this assumption to the generations that followed. Yet I always made that mistake. The public demands are never perfectly known and cannot be accurately forecasted. Some men, though seeking with fervor to use their knowledge, abilities, and available capital for profit and accumulation of wealth, will make mistakes or miss random chances and become poor instead. Other men who somehow correctly match their opportunities and hunches to the market get rich. I would too often presume all men must belong in one or the other of these categories, assigning to them various amounts of talents and apportionments of luck.

But E's citizens constituted a third class. This group of individuals wished to avoid all of these risks. What they wanted was to sell their services at a guaranteed wage, forfeiting, in return for this security, the opportunity to become wealthy. These individuals gave the right to make the decisions to others, their employers or their government, and were satisfied to do so. Once enough feel this way, then there are others who will follow, either out of failure to perceive an alternative or because the example looks good to them. The young pessimist, perhaps without realizing it, will see who about him seems to be content, who nervous and worried, who successful, and who unsuccessful. When surrounded by people who are not risk-takers but rather searchers for security, many youngsters may never meet a successful and happy risk-taker face to face.

I did not enjoy it but I had to accept that what was happening on E, an increasingly firm dependency on government central planning and a diminished interest in free enterprise, was not strange. It was one of the natural possibilities for a society of men.

Chapter XI

The Free Island
of MY

WHEN WE LAST DISCUSSED the island of MY they were in terrible condition, in the peak of their economic depression of the 1780s. Currency inflation was completely out of control, with paper bills that no one wanted much of being printed abundantly. For their day-to-day activities they were almost back to barter arrangements. Both production and living standards had dropped badly. The government and the citizens alike were confused as to the purpose and value of money and they were depressed in spirit as well as in credit and personal wealth.

As I observed all of this—and pondered it with the knowledge of CONO's and E's prior depressions and their welcome, beginning recoveries—I hoped that some way would be found by MY's leaders to accelerate their return to economic health. Moreover, I really did not approve of either CONO's or E's attempts at arriving at an improved, "non-depression" economy and was not anxious to find MY duplicating either's approach. CONO was wishy-washy, with some government control and regulation, some free enterprise, and much remaining lack of clarity or good basic ideas on what constitutes economic soundness. E was even worse, so far as I could see, what with its virtually total commitment to government direction of the economy and the consequent demoting of free enterprise. I wanted for the island of MY something different and better.

I felt confident I could design for them an improved economic system. It was tremendously frustrating for me to be isolated as an observer up in the sky. I wished I had the power to descend and change places with one of the more influential leaders. I thought about what I would say, how by my extraordinary urgings and logic I would get the economy flowing. In fact, I even chose a specific leader, Alfredo Rosa, whose place I would like to take for only a few weeks. He had the greatest forcefulness of character on MY. He was remarkably articulate in his speech, had dignity and firmness of manner, and his reputation for both intellect and compassion was of the highest.

It was when I forced myself to detail in my mind precisely what I would do, how I would do it, with whom I would communicate, that I made the discovery of a power that has served me so well in the decades since. I found that this very man, Rosa, began to say and do exactly what I wished he would.

Rosa called together the other leaders, the owners of industry, the recognized professional experts, and those looked up to as the wisest men and women of the community. He included the young and more vociferous complainers who, though lacking respect now for their elders, whom they held responsible for the lack of jobs and opportunity, nevertheless had vim and vitality and an innate desire to make things happen again in their society.

He said, as I hoped he would, "Look here. You had a system that worked for decades. Granted it is defective or it could not have led to the present situation, is it reasonable to believe it is totally unsound and must be rejected in its entirety? Let us retrace our steps, planning tentatively to do again what we did on this island when our grandparents and their parents settled here. Then let us reason out what else we must do, what we must do differently, what mistakes we must not repeat, if we are to avoid in the future the massive depression that has befallen us.

"First," I said to them through the brain and voice of Rosa, "let us recall all of the currency that is outstanding. It has become nearly worthless anyway. Then let us again establish by government edict a new, useful account in the bank for all. We shall choose a sensible value for the dollar as our forefathers did, roughly the pay for a day's work, and give every one a month's supply. Let the government accept those dollars as taxes and let everyone be taxed so that there will be a government fund again to carry on government projects, to buy food for the temporarily unemployed, to pay for school-teachers' salaries, to repair and maintain the water and sewage systems. Again, as before, we shall have no base for the currency. However, and especially this time around, we shall be sure we possess the most careful control over the amount of currency and credit that we shall issue. We shall appoint a council of our top economists to figure out the right beginning deposits for each of us. They will see that too great a demand will not be created because of too much money in circulation competing for too small a supply of the goods and services which we all need. The economic council will set up loans to all businesses in a sensible relation to their cash needs. Let us all take a pledge to accept the new currency. We shall come together as a united nation and assign an interest in our accumulated wealth to all.

"Similarly we shall set for a time a specific rate of interest. We shall put enough money in circulation in this way so that we can commence to buy from one another. We shall fix prices by law on critical items—a medium-sized fish, a pair of shoes, a loaf of bread, a pint of oil, a day's work as a carpenter. This will be a temporary and emergency procedure. When we have put everyone to work providing what he or she needs, then we shall gradually drop all of these controls and go back to the free market."

But some of the other leaders, young and old, stepped forward immediately and said, "Rosa, you disappoint us. You have not suggested enough that is different from what was done by our first settlers. Surely, we must have more deviations from our approach of the last several decades or history will repeat. Another depression in a decade or two will catch our children and grandchildren with their greater population and with more severe effect."

These and other questions had me worried. I was the center of attention, what with the fervor of my speaking and the eminent position of Alfredo Rosa which I had usurped, and yet I realized I had not thoroughly thought out my case. I stalled by giving them a forceful rendition of the best of my essays on free enterprise, some that I presented often on board ship to the parents and grandparents of some of my audience. I was good at this and it held them for a short while.

The best system, I told them, was still one that stressed the maximum of freedom for each individual to contribute the most as he saw fit, to take risks, to innovate, to expand the economy for everyone's benefit by his personal advance. Just before this line could become completely tiresome to my auditors, I shifted the subject to blaming the recent government for its lack of sound participation, its foolish action in place of that minimum and intelligent control which it should have exercised.

I claimed the real catastrophe was not the overexpansion of the economy before the downturn. The private economy, I assured them, has a natural tendency toward stability. It would have straightened itself out in a short while. But the government had gone ahead to expand the currency crazily, devaluing the dollar with its overprinting. All that was really needed was sensible action by the government to see that the money supply was about right, not too much and not too little. It should have done this by early action instead of a late overreaction.

By this time I had recovered a bit in assembling my thoughts and was ready to focus on the questions that they had asked. What should we do on MY that is different from what the original island settlers did? Only a modest difference will assure freedom from another panic, I told them. First, we need to control the money supply. Of course, a government bank must exist, but it should not be involved in lending to individuals or private companies. It should only lend to private banks. It should do so at interest rates set by the government and, of course, it should be the sole source of the printing of currency. What sort of regulation of private banks is required? Each private bank must keep on deposit with the government bank a substantial fraction of all of the money that it gets hold of, whether its own or that of its depositors. The government bank should regulate. That is, it should determine the fraction of the assets of private banks that must be so deposited in this reserve.

A very alert, continual observation of the money supply should be carried on by the government. It should always know approximately the amount of currency in circulation, the amount of deposits in the banks, and the buildup of credit. If the government bank and the private banks lend out too much, this might give rise to too much money in circulation. On the other hand, we should recognize that there will be a need for a steadily rising money stock. More goods will have to be produced as population rises. Also the application of new ideas and facilities for producing more per worker—in other words, heightened productivity—will increase the gross national production. If there is not enough money to feed these dimensions of natural growth, it will be stifled. Thus we need just the right balance of money supply, business expansion, population growth, and productivity increase.

"How shall we know how much money should be out in

circulation? How will the government banker know to what extent he should limit credit?" they asked. To this I replied that as a beginning measure a government staff should observe prices of quite stable items. Suppose the prices of shoes rise. The government should ask, "Is this because there is a shortage of leather, because too few people are available to make shoes, or too few employed by the shoemaker who is too conservative and fears to increase production?" Perhaps they will discover it is merely that we are undergoing a steady inflation on MY because of too much money being fed into the system, creating a desire in everyone to purchase new shoes with no practical comparable growth in capacity to produce them? Surely, watching the prices will be a clue, and sound analysis can follow. The government can always increase interest rates on its loans to private banks and tell the private banks to lend out less of their available funds and thus curb the inflation.

"But there is something else that the government can do," I postulated to them. "The government spends money, which it should obtain by taxing the people. As a healthy economy grows, the government will have more tax money, this in proportion to growth in the income of the people and the profits of business, two good indicators of economic health. The government will then be able to spend more to improve our schools and to build new ones as more young children are born. We shall improve our roads and keep them in repair and this also will require additional money each year because more people will travel on the roads and wear them down. Now suppose we find that there is inflation, prices rising, businesses having to pay more for their labor, consumers having to pay more for the same article. Then we should tax more, to remove some of that excess money in circulation. We should cut government spending, deferring until a later time some expenditures needed for the island as a whole. Conversely, if we find prices falling, we can ease up on credit restrictions, encouraging borrowing, and increase government spending."

As I told them all this and obtained their acceptance, and the island went to work again and began to build up the economy following my recommendations, it suddenly occurred to me that what I had caused them to do was not so different from what had been done already on CONO. I had convinced myself and MY that free use of private capital and individual initiative, with only a minimum of absolutely essential government control, was the best approach. Then had I not blithely stumbled into detailing my views with suggestions of rather considerable governmental involvement?

I knew my proposals had not even remotely recommended the non-free-enterprise economy set up by E. But could I really claim that CONO, where there were no wage and price fixings but only government control of the money supply, had failed to show an adequate interest in free enterprise? Much of the answer was provided by the actual experience of the next few years. The leadership on MY proceeded to arrange the absolute minimum of government intervention. Those few people working for the government who were supposed to be watching the private banks did so with great casualness, not even requiring large reserves on their part. What they did about interest rates when the government bank lent money to the private banks was little more than merely to respond with supply to demand. On CONO, in contrast, there was a serious regard for the importance of control of the money supply, both in the interest of preventing a new depression from forming and to promote the most rapidly growing economy.

Why did not MY then develop intolerably big swings in supply and demand, in production overcapacity versus the real requirement, and all the rest of the cyclic characteristics of a free economy that could become unstable? Why did not MY go into another intolerable downturn within another few years or a decade or two?

They didn't. Perhaps, as I had preached, a great deal of

self-correcting truly does exist in a free economy. But, of course, that is not a good enough answer. It happened before, and it could happen again. Could it be that what held back a dangerous overheating of the economy, or an equally unacceptable cooling down to a stalled freeze, was the ever-present threat of government action to control credit and stop overexpansion, or, on the other hand, to expand credit and accelerate the economy if it appeared to be slowing down too rapidly? A little action by the government took place occasionally and the possibility of greater action was recognized by all. Some swings did get started that looked precarious for a while and the government then did adjust reserve requirements in the private banks. It did control the government budget of expenditures and taxation to a slight extent in response, and it did alter interest rates in its loans to the private banks. Maybe small actions by government only infrequently are all that are ever needed to keep a good free enterprise economy going smoothly.

Something else I observed too: the experience of the 1780s on MY caused all of the private banks to be more conservative. They were careful not to lend out quite so much of their deposits. They kept a larger reserve, quite apart from the looking-over-the-shoulder by the government. All businesses were a little more carefully run, not allowing themselves to operate with quite so much debt, a little more cautious about the possibility of overexpansion. Finally, the government of MY kept its budget in balance. As on the island of CONO and on the island of E, the government of MY made the usual expenditures for the common services of education, water supply, communications, parks, and waste removal. But unlike the island of E, where government expenditures were relatively high, and CONO where, we might say, they were medium, government expenditures on MY were remarkably low. The government did the least and MY's public expected private activities to take care of everything possible. It was always understood that taxes should be low so that, with the commitment to have government income and outgo in balance and with deficits unacceptable, the expenditures had to be low.

For example, on the island of MY, in contrast with CONO and E, there was no unemployment relief. Someone in financial difficulty could look to his relatives to help or his friends or private charities. Charity and social service were not regarded as proper roles for government. Private schools were common, so even government expenditure for education was at a minimum. A company using water in its production would expect to drill wells on its land on MY, or locate next to a stream, whereas on CONO about half the time and on E all of the time it was understood that water would be furnished by the government.

A conspicuous difference between CONO and MY was that CONO was on the gold standard while nothing was behind MY's currency. But what each government was doing about the economy was almost the same, with more reluctance and casualness on MY. If I was right in my lectures, and so influenced beneficially the setting up of both recovery and permanent economic growth on the island of MY, then apparently whether or not there was gold in the treasury was unimportant. The currency possessing a base, the piece of paper having a meaning in the sense of its representing something being held in the government bank, apparently did not matter greatly.

When I began to puzzle about this, my concern rose again about the island of E with its strict control. E used land, or thought it used land, as a base for the currency, but that in itself was not what led E to government control. Had I believed in it I could have lectured MY to set up a tightly controlled economy, completely emulating the island of E, without ever mentioning the use of land as a base for the currency. If there is no confidence in the control of the money supply, if the proper government rules and regulations do not exist on extending bank credit and printing money, then it does not matter whether there is land or gold or nothing as a money supply. The economy will be in a mess in any case.

One could always expect swings in the economic system, ups and downs in supply and demand, productivity shifts, bad fishing weather, technological developments, or a host of other changing factors. Must these trigger instabilities that might build up and result in runaway effects, depressions, economic panics, ruination of the economic system, failure to employ everyone usefully, and to get on with growth of the economy? No. Prevention of disasters traces back to having the right kind of combination, a hybrid, if you will, of free enterprise and governmental control. Free individual action employed to the fullest advantage and, at the same time, the citizens acting as a group through their government to set the rules for that free personal action—this was the formula I found myself favoring.

By 1785, all three islands were out of their big depressions and growing in a more or less steady way. Each island had departed from all-out free enterprise. They had different money systems and the extent of governmental direction of the economy was in the order from most to least: E, CONO, and MY. And now I was left with increased curiosity, a need to see how the three economies would grow and prosper. What would be the extent of instabilities, the degree of unemployment, the number of times in which dislocating inflation or deflation would occur as the decades changed to a century on all three of my islands with their variances in the handling of the partnership of free enterprise and governmental control? Which island would show up best? Would there be a difference? I was not confident I knew. Maybe developing events would make it all clear.

Chapter XII

The Quest for
Economic Growth

E, CONO, AND MY shared an extraordinary interest in economic growth. The leaders on all three islands preached that an ever-expanding economy was good. In their varying ways, the citizens and their governments acted on the idea. At the first of each year, they would look at the previous year's accomplishments, the amount of goods produced, and the improved facilities created. The average income per person on the islands and the productivity were noted and increases were celebrated. The islands differed in their means for assessing gross national economic status but that did not matter much, so far as I could tell. All three kept track of the total spending by government, business, and consumers for all goods and services. They even allowed for inflation (or deflation) as they gathered their statistics. They realized prices might have been bid up artificially for certain products that happened to be in temporary short supply. Thus, it would not do to assume they had produced more just because the total of dollars expended on these items might have turned out greater. They tried to assess what they had really accomplished, even though the price of the accomplishment varied up and down.

"What is the formula for economic growth?" I continually asked myself. I understood some of the aspects of this question, but certainly not all. To obtain growth, it is necessary to be willing to invest in the future. This I was certain of. If one spends everything that he earns, then his savings will not grow. If a business, after paying for all of the costs of interest, materiel, and wages, finds it has something left over as a profit and proceeds to give all these earnings to the owners as a reward for their having invested, then it has nothing left to build a bigger plant for more production or to design new products that will increase its sales. Growth requires investment.

Suppose a fisherman on one of the islands catches 100 fish a week. Instead of fishing, he might take one week off to make a big fishnet. This net, we can say, will have cost him those 100 fish. But imagine that with his new net he can now increase his weekly fish catch to 150. Over the following two weeks he will have recovered his loss of 100 fish and be even in total fish take. From then on, or as long as the net lasts, his investment will have put him into a higher category. He will have grown to being a 150-catch fisherman instead of a 100-catch fisherman, and he will be booking the additional profit each week.

What should the fisherman now do with his increased earnings? Should he build still another fishnet? Possibly. But he should not make such additional investments indefinitely. He will reach a point of diminishing returns. As more nets are added to the business, it will be true eventually that still one more net will not yield enough in return to pay for its cost to him. It will be better for him to put his excess, discretionary resources into something else. At some point it will be better for him to deposit them in the bank and collect some interest on the deposit. Ultimately the law of diminishing returns on investments will set the rate of interest in a free market situation.

Of course, our fisherman need not have taken off a week to make his net. He could have hired someone else to do it, or he could have borrowed the price of the net from the bank and bought a net if he had a good enough story. So we see credit and capital availability and use of resources or savings for immediate consumption versus investment in the future combining to set a growth pattern in the economy.

To what extent is governmental intervention in this process good or bad? Why should not free enterprise and a free market be the best stimulants and determinants for maximum growth? To answer my own questions, I had to note that the moment money supply control, bank credit control, reserve policy for banks, and the like are even partially in the hands of government, even though presumably only to avoid a future big depression, then government is inevitably involved in growth of the economy. We come down then to the issue of how to arrange government's contribution so as to add security without curbing growth, preferably to stimulate it. Again, we seek the right amount of government control, not too much, not too little, and the right quality or kind of governmental influence.

I could readily identify more reasons why the government's policies and actions would affect economic development, whether I liked it or not. For instance, human resources are second to none in their effect on economic growth. Investing in human beings increases their productivity. Better education of the young people on the island and more training of workers require investment in school buildings and in wages for teachers. In the short term, it is costly to the island's economy to provide for the training of the citizens of the future who, when better trained, will hopefully produce more later than has been spent preparing them earlier for this increase. On all three islands the government was involved in this education and training program, so the government's budget for education was a factor in setting the ultimate growth rate of the economy.

The least of this kind of government partnership in investment in human resources was on the island of MY where there were more private schools and more small businesses that handled their own training of apprentices than on CONO or E. One could argue here again that free enterprise or individual initiative is adequate. Heads of families and people who run businesses will invest to educate their children and workers. So the argument becomes one of whether or not private versus public schooling and training is the more efficient way to provide for this kind of investment in the future.

In almost every facet of the economy, I could work up an argument with myself on the most advantageous degree of government involvement in economic growth. But I lacked the experimental results. The best way to obtain them, I decided, was for me to go on observing the islands, comparing their varying accomplishments against the extent to which the governments were factors in economic planning and control.

On the island of CONO, where technological development was much more advanced than on the other two islands, the people took special pride in the introduction of new products and in the development of machines that would produce more with less manual effort. Investment in new technology as a way to growth was an enthusiastically accepted approach on CONO. They were particularly interested in increasing productivity. They believed every hour of work should accomplish more each year through increased know-how and better tools. With the development of fertilizers, machines for processing fish, better schemes for producing cloth, agricultural tools, glass, bricks, numerous devices for preparing leather and making shoes, and the like, they could show a gain that was greater than the growth of the population in the total amount of goods and services produced. Where in the 1740s typical individuals on the island, men, women, and children, owned one pair of shoes, fifty years later each person now possessed two or three pairs. They were able to do this, not only because their earnings were higher but because shoes were actually cheaper, the way in which they were made having greatly altered.

On CONO, technological development and invention were a route to wealth. Individuals and companies prospered by exploiting imagination and advancing technology. Those connected with technology—the entrepreneurs, engineers, financial arrangement-makers who brought in investments from all over the island to back up a new venture—were looked up to with great respect. They were models for the young. Leaders of the technological industry had great influence in the government. Professional politicians understood and orated about the importance of productivity increases. New laws considered for passage were scrutinized to be sure that they did not handicap economic growth but instead gave ample opportunity to stimulate free enterprise and enhance motivation with the idea of getting the maximum of economic gain.

On the island of E, where there was tight governmental regulation of everything, loud calls were heard also for a high gross national product. But it was the government that did the calling, perpetually campaigning for higher productivity and preaching motivation. It set up a system of medals for individuals who had shown unusual desire to work hard and produce more in the factories. Annual prizes were awarded for the best technological inventions. The government included in its budget the sponsoring of research and development intended to advance the island's technology and, hence, its economic growth.

However, E's economic growth and technological development lagged greatly behind CONO's. We have already discussed the lack of motivation owing to a lack of incentive. Medals were not enough. Because of the depth of governmental regulation, the habit grew of looking to the government to provide answers to every problem and to satisfy every citizen demand. With the government controlling so thoroughly, with wages and prices fixed in narrow ranges, profits and credit granting carefully analyzed by government, and approvals required for expansion by industry, one began to feel he was as much entitled to fair rewards as his neighbor regardless of individual contribution. The system made uniformity, not exceptional performance, a virtue, even if unintentionally.

Typically, on the island of E, politicians would promise greater supplies of all goods and services for everyone when they ran for office. Later, in trying to make good on the promises or in preparing to defend their record for the next election, the officeholders would press the citizens to produce and invent more, increase quality, and work hard. But at the same time the system minimized the rewards, and that is what counted most. The island of E was interested in economic growth, technological development, increased productivity, and material production for its citizens. At least, the government kept telling the islanders this was so. However, E succeeded in getting far less of what they insisted they sought than CONO did.

The island of MY, we are reminded, had even less governmental interference with the economy than did the island of CONO. I had seen to that. Theirs were only the minimum controls needed to eliminate the possibility of a massive depression. Money supply, we recall, was controlled, as on CONO, and wages and prices were not, again as on CONO. However, the overall economic growth of the island of MY was less than that of CONO, although better than that of E.

The difference between MY's and CONO's economic growth, it seemed to me, came directly from the superiority of CONO's technology. How did this happen? It was in part the original impetus of the exceptional capability of the particular group that happened to come on my ships rather on the ships of MY. This was accidental for I had tried to even out the talent. It just turned out, apparently by chance, that more of the better inventors, metallurgists, chemists, agricultural experts, and machine designers appeared to have been on the CONO ships and they made more rapid progress than their counterparts on the other two islands. Moreover, by coincidence, the minerals needed for technological advance were more readily available on or near the surface on the island of CONO. Perhaps I should note also that CONO's temperature was a bit cooler, so there was less tendency to play on the beach there than on the islands of E and MY.

Another reason for MY's growth being slower than CONO's was the culture that had developed on MY. Maybe that was my fault. From the 1780s onward MY's citizens developed great devotion to the idea that the government should be as unnoticeable as possible, surfacing only if a severe depression threatened. CONO, though its was far from the severe governmental regulation of E, nevertheless participated in overall economic planning and in exhorting the citizens to advance. MY's citizens would have rebelled at the CONO government's propaganda for growth and its analyzing of the economy. Of course, they would have found E's controlled economy utterly absurd and worth only total rejection. On MY, everyone did his own thing.

If MY had an economic religion, maximum freedom, CONO made technological development a way of life. Worship of technology was CONO's creed. There was a zeal to invent and raise the standard of living, to acquire more, to do more with the resources, so government leadership became closely tied to technological, private industry leadership. In contrast, on the island of MY those individuals aspired to and were elected to office who believed in the government's leaving things alone. On MY the leaders never talked about a government program to increase productivity, even though they thought productivity and technological development to be good things.

CONO's superiority in technology I regarded as evidence of the superiority of free enterprise. Few innovations, I knew from my industrial experience in Spain, are uncovered by serendipity. It is only in fairy tales that great discoveries are commonly made by accident. In real life it very seldom happens. Most scientific and technological progress is the result of long and painstaking thought and experiments. The work is characterized by failures and disappointments. As long as the ideas, when successful, are eventually marketable at a high profit, then research and engineering efforts toward innovation will be induced by the rewards of the market-place. These rewards sometimes have to appear enormous because only large gains will compensate for large risks of failure and the high costs of some projects even when successful.

On the island of E, appreciation of the importance of innovation existed on the part of the government and the citizens. But the reward to seek innovation was minimal. The certainty was maximum that profits resulting from the inno-vative effort would be quickly limited through energetic price-fixing by government.

On CONO, there was no such problem. CONO even developed a pattern of teaming up of several sources of capital to provide for the large pool of funds needed to handle large projects. The reward and risk ratio were in good match on CONO, whether for small or large projects. In contrast, the casualness of approach and the independence of the people on MY lent themselves well to small-scale innova-tion. Brilliant, wide, creative departures, including techno-logical advances, were common on MY, but inclined to be limited to those projects that would not require a great deal of capital. CONO had less of a limit here. E was least innovative and least technological.

MY's individualistic approach to life, its freedom for its citizens, showed itself in the large number of small businesses that characterized its structure. CONO and E both had big companies and large farms by the early 1800s. On CONO, concepts of maximum return on private investment and rapid economic growth forced it, because often size went with payout. On E, government control militated toward large consolidated entities seeking higher productivity and effi-ciency, though seldom attaining it.

People were more artistically creative on MY. There

were cleverly designed and artistic clocks, lamps, utensils, and wearing apparel, all handmade, individual, one of a kind. Ingenious tools were designed to aid the craftsmen in the use of their hands, and relatively little attention was given to the design of machines to make possible large quantity manufacture. Even in food, it was MY which produced innovative products, an amazing variety, each little farmer, baker, winemaker, goat cheese producer, or pig meat or fish smoker, preferring to create his own version and taking pride in his product. The idea was not unthought of, of course, of pooling together the efforts of many to arrive at a more efficient operation, standardizing the product, using the cost reduction benefit of high volume, repetitive operations, and obtaining the advantages of distribution of an established product over the whole island. The people of MY simply preferred otherwise; they developed a preoccupation with the concept of everyone doing what suited him most. They loved the diversity, novelty, and changing forms, choosing these over the cheaper but more constant items issuing from more centralized production.

Perhaps this approach to life was also a factor in MY's not experiencing a repeat of their big depression. As their population grew so did the range and spread of small business activities. Large rises and falls would tend to get diffused in the many offsets of ripples and swings of so fractionized an economy.

Every once in a while on the island of MY a politician would arise who would decide the government was not doing enough to stimulate the most rapid growth of the economy. To MY voters, the political candidate who preached this line was likely to be the victim of a landslide in favor of his opponent. But one exceptionally charismatic individual spouting this general approach—a handsome young man by the name of Simon Lase-Ferrer—campaigned on a specific new idea in 1825. He said the citizens were not investing enough in growth. The government should provide some bonds which would pay an interest rate higher than that of the banks. It would be different from a bank deposit in that the citizens, having purchased these bonds, would expect to hold them for a five-year period, after which the government would buy them back for a higher price.

The other half of his bold program had to do with the government's use of the money thus collected. Lase-Ferrer's thinking was that first the government would eliminate taxes. (Perhaps it has occurred to you that Lase-Ferrer appreciated there might be some voter enthusiasm for this.) The government would no longer need tax revenues, since adequate funds would be available from the sale of the government bonds. With individuals and businesses relieved of taxes, they could plow back tax money into building their businesses. More economic growth would result, he pointed out, causing everyone to get richer. Meanwhile, they would all be saving money because they would be receiving their money back on the bonds, plus a generous amount of interest, five years later. Here and there during the campaign, Lase-Ferrer was asked what would happen five years later. Where would the government get the money to pay back everyone? He answered that it would at that time sell even more government bonds for the succeeding five years, since a good idea such as this should be continued.

Lase-Ferrer was elected and his plan was put into effect. But MY's citizens were accustomed to making their own decisions about their individual businesses. Only a portion of the savings available from reduced taxes was put into business investment for future growth, about the same amount as the typical MY entrepreneur had previously planned. His investment policy had always been based solely on his judgment of what he thought was the real market growth potential for his product, and he was influenced little by theoretical speculations tied to Lase-Ferrer's new government bonds idea. The surplus savings of MY's citizens and business, resulting from the sudden tax relief, were put into the banks. Lase-Ferrer found that government bonds were not selling too well, and the government budget seemed to be in danger, what with the tax cut already implemented and the bond income to the government proving disappointing. So he persuaded the government to increase the interest rate offered on the further sale of bonds, that is, to increase the payback price promised for five years later.

The banks responded by increasing their interest rate on deposits in the same proportion. Fortunately for Lase-Ferrer, his announcement of decreased taxes had in effect increased the opportunity of the MY citizens to save, had put more money into the savings banks than they could readily lend out and this money supply-demand condition soon tended to press interest rates back down and encouraged purchase of his bonds by those who sought the highest interest income. The play of the free market on availability of capital had provided neutralizing forces and stabilized interest rates, so they neither rose nor fell very much. The only trouble was that the stabilization took a while and resulted in the government's temporarily having less funds and the private banks holding more of the island's money with less of it lent out than before. This distortion or perturbation of free market financial forces by a government action created no permanent impairment of MY's economic health. What about more investment in growth, the big change Lase-Ferrer was seeking? Capital spending for growth increased hardly at all. The only clear result of Lase-Ferrer's plan was that the government was in trouble for a while with regard to its income and expenditure budget and Lase-Ferrer was in trouble with his career.

By the next year, when Lase-Ferrer was replaced by Exchequieros de Stricto, the government of MY went back to taxing the people. Government bonds, however, continued to be a useful, parallel way for the government to raise money. With bonds it could fund present activities by borrowing from the people against the future.

So I understood that each island wanted economic growth; each island, in the late 1700s and early 1800s took pride in its increase in gross national product (speaking of

LASE-FERRER | EXCHEQUIEROS de STRICTO

the real growth, not the imaginary, artificial growth expressed in dollars if it was simply the result of price inflation). However, the islands were realizing a different degree of growth. I knew by now that the differences in growth rates attained were dependent upon many things. It was not just the result of the technology on CONO, as I had first thought, for example. It was also the individualism on MY, and the restrictions and inhibitions and excessive governmental control on E. It was these things, and it was more, and it was everything all taken together, some factors accidental, some the result of variances in their systems, some the result of differing resources or people.

But I was more than curious about one aspect. This was the extent of the effect of a government's intervention into the economy on the economic growth. Rate the three islands in economic growth: as the 1700s came to an end, it was

CONO first, MY second, and E, third. Population growth had something to do with this, of course, and so did available natural resources.

On population, it was E first, MY second, and CONO third—so no one could claim that CONO led because it had more people. As to natural resources, as near as I could tell it had been essentially a toss-up at the beginning. However, as the new century was about to open, CONO led in the using up of its available minerals and E had used the least. In technological advancement, the order was CONO first, followed by MY, and then by E. We might be tempted to say that technology appeared to lead both to economic growth and to the using up of resources.

Now, what about governmental intervention? We had MY with the least governmental influence and E with the most effort by government in trying to manage the economy. My bias naturally caused me to assume that E, by being last in economic growth, had proved that too much governmental control stymies economic growth. But if this was a valid conclusion, why did the island of MY, with its least of all butting-in by government, with its maximum of free enterprise, lag in growth behind the island of CONO? Was it because technological development is the biggest factor transcending government interference, population growth, natural resources? Maybe, but the way in which government interferes in the economy must have a great deal to do with how much technological development can be expected, just as it has a great deal to do with motivation of individuals and business organizations.

So, as the 1700s ended, I still needed to know more than I did about how best to run a free-enterprise, or a partially free-enterprise, economy. Sooner or later, I hoped, it would be possible to see from the islands' experience what was important and what was not. Perhaps a few decades of the 1800s would suffice to show me the proper role of free enterprise and government in attaining maximum economic growth.

Chapter XIII

The Inflation Battle

IN THE FIRST DECADE of the 1800s, I had not yet perceived that the most interesting issue soon would become not economic growth by itself but the contest to control inflation. I devoted a lot of time during those years to daydreaming about what I would do or say if I could drop down and take the place of the leadership of the islands. I assumed I still had this power whenever I wanted to use it. If I could enter the brains of the political bosses or top bankers or businessmen or perhaps of enough of the citizens, what would I change to attain the greatest economic growth?

Some things I could readily accomplish, albeit at some risk. For instance, I could arrange for the government bank to extend credit to assist every entrepreneur to expand to the fullest. Let there never be anyone unemployed because there is no one to employ him. That is wasteful. Let every factory and every farm use every available worker. If the employer lacks the tools or the facilities or the money with which to pay the new employee, let me lend him the money from the government bank.

You see now why I have mentioned the word "risk" almost immediately. Be assured I understood that if I extended credit too generously, to be sure of the maximum expansion of the economy by using every man and every facility and every idea to the fullest, then I would certainly inflate the economy. Too much money would be put out in the system by such liberal extensions of credit. Some of my credit granting would certainly stimulate overexpansion. Too many bigger factories would be erected and the public simply would not need or desire to buy many of the extra items produced. With workers in scarce supply, because there would not be enough to go around to all the enlarging businesses, the entrepreneurs would bid up wages, literally buying employees away from each other. This would increase costs, which would shortly increase asking prices. The resultant supply, too large for the demand, would lead eventually to a price drop, of course, and bank loans that could not be paid back.

By attempting to use every bit of credit that I could extend to finance the greatest expansion of the economy, I would create inflation. That inflation might, a bit later, trigger a big depression. Even if I were stupid enough to try it, I doubt if I could enter enough brains, in view of the experiences of the past, the lessons learned and still remembered, to cause the citizens and leadership groups of any of the three islands to follow me in this course.

But I really was not interested in experimenting with this kind of extreme. I wanted only to raise the question of how much credit expansion, under the careful control of all three governments through their handling of the money supply, should be permitted. Should I really try, as they were doing on the island of E, to stop inflation altogether? Isn't a little inflation acceptable? Isn't there an amount of inflation that is tolerable, an amount of risk I could take with regard to triggering a depression that would give me maximum growth of the economy? If a depression starts building, it is only required that it not do so too rapidly, or so quietly and unnoticed, as to get away from me. I could always step in, could I not, and pull back on credit and cut the money supply's growth?

One thing penalizing about inflation is that not all can anticipate it. If they have not planned for it and substantial inflation occurs, they may suffer greatly in their finances, especially relative to others who have been good guessers. When people expect inflation, they will clamor for loans. They will buy things ahead of need, often on credit, wishing to avoid the higher prices they believe will be certain to come later. Anyone in the business of lending money will demand a higher premium or interest rate before he will grant a loan, because he expects it to be paid with inflated dollars which will be worth less in buying power at that later, payback time.

If everyone could anticipate inflation accurately and then take steps to protect himself, then inflation would probably be avoided, or the inflation that would occur, if it is the amount expected, would leave everyone even. But in real life not everyone has the privilege of adjusting his situation, even if he were possessed of a perfect vision of the future. Particularly is this true of someone living on a fixed income.

Granted government participation, what is the proper degree of action, the right money supply increase to arrange, the perfect degree of credit to extend? What is the best amount of reserve to require the private banks to have on deposit with the government bank, the rest of their assets being lent out? What acts will stimulate growth with the proper balance against tolerable risk and controllable inflation?

What about the optimum level to choose for government spending, which is a major factor in money supply? The government can enter the economy directly by being a sponsor of technological development and, hence, of productivity increases. It can spend for better schools, an improved educational process, and more teachers. More training should presumably provide more skilled citizens who would produce and invent more. They would innovate more and think better, and their judgment would be superior. Government programs, if well chosen and implemented, should create more goods and valuable services per person at some time in the future. People could then pay higher taxes to finance still greater government programs.

How about investment by government in the health of the citizens, in studying the causes of disease, in increasing the number of years that a person can produce and contribute to the economy? Or how about the government's studying initiative and incentive in people, learning what makes people more productive? How many hours per week should workers work as against the number of their play hours to provide the combination of health and mental attitude that would produce more? The government could study and investigate these matters and the results of the study could be put to advantage. But, unless it did so carefully as to budget, government action and expenditure following the study could cause inflation.

But the government's budget isn't needed, I decided, to ensure technological developments. Free enterprise is certainly another way. For many aspects, I felt certain, it is the best way. True, private entrepreneurs will only put their money into developing new technology if it appears they will profit from it. Furthermore, some technological developments will be of such nature that they are important to the island as a whole but are not attractive to the profit-seeking financial backer. For instance, on CONO in 1810 there was great interest in using basic oil and glass components, together with metals and chemicals of various kinds, to produce materials that were strong, could substitute for wood, and be created not only in long cords and fibers but also in plates and strips tough enough to build the surface structure of a seagoing boat. Here the entrepreneur backers of the inventors could see many uses for their new robust materials and they expected to reap profits by investment in this new technology. On the other hand, improving the water supply on CONO by superior ways of constructing the dams and reservoirs to provide water reserves and arrange pressure for easy flow to the homes and factories was unlikely without a government program.

The CONO government was known to the producers as being perhaps the least attractive of all customers, exerting its strong position to force its bias for low profits. Its negotiations were public and subject to political and bureaucratic maneuvering and scrutiny. The leading glass window manufacturer on CONO in 1810, Carlos del Vista, knew that if he made glass windows for factories and homes, he could obtain a better profit on his investment than if he made windows for schools, but he contracted to do the latter anyway. A politician, Frederico Expositas, a little later claimed that there was excess profit made through the school window contract going to Carlos and called attention to the fact that Carlos's relative, Francisco del Vista, was the head of the school system. It was rumored that Francisco received some money back on the quiet in payment for a bias toward his cousin in granting the window contract.

Carlos later refunded some of the funds he received, and anyone on CONO who sold glass windows to the schools afterward was regarded with suspicion. The seller had to lean over backward to assure everyone that he made only a minimum profit. He had to prove to Exposita's committee that he was honest and had no relatives in the pertinent government posts.

Some needs of all the citizens, bought by their government under special rules and scrutiny, would not necessarily be developed or available at all if private industry were the only source of investment to provide the required capability. Accordingly, I am back now to the idea that the government is a necessary sponsor of some technological growth. But then I am back also to the question of how the government obtains funds for it without causing inflation. Could I look for the answer to E, where the government was busy holding down prices and also engaged in sponsoring technological development? Not really, because E's growth was so poor. E's growth was the lowest because there government action amounted to restriction on growth. Quite apart from the loss of motivation and incentive resulting from overly tight governmental control, it was the objective of the rules that hurt the economy. The government tried to attain a zero risk of runaway inflation or of any serious instability of the economy that might come from overexpansion. Trying for no risk of "overdoing" netted them a steady "underdoing." Furthermore, E's government was against profit, always squeezing it to hold prices down. They thus demotivated investors and obtained less growth.

A reasonable profit, reinvested, would have developed technology on E that could have lowered prices and expanded the economy. Growth was attained on CONO because the government was far less restrictive. True, in addition, CONO's technological development was superior. Yet, it seemed that CONO's subdued governmental action and greater reliance on free enterprise was a factor in their realizing this technological development.

On the island of MY, the government was involved in the economy so little that free enterprise could have and should have blossomed there fully. Why didn't it? At times on the island of MY, the economy would temporarily slow down, a part of the natural cycling, the accumulation of supply and demand imbalances, and of misjudgments here and there. On similar occasions, the island of CONO's leadership would expand credit, having in mind that the government had an obligation to act to sustain high economic growth. By contrast, on the island of MY, the government took no action unless it looked as though the slowdown was going to be catastrophic. When they did then take action, expanding credit somewhat, lowering the interest rate at the government bank, increasing government spending by catching up with needed public facilities or easing up on taxes so there would be more spending money in circulation, they did it at the last possible moment. On the island of MY, the government was not regarded as having a duty to participate in ensuring high economic growth.

On E, the government fought inflation as though every percentage point in price rises was a defeat in a battle. They tightly controlled the economy with the effect of keeping prices stable, rather than the economy growing, even though they talked growth. On CONO, the government tried to stay out and give the free market economy the maximum chance, but it acted quickly and forcefully whenever the growth tended to fall off, without waiting for a major slack in the economy. CONO's game, one they wanted to win, was economic growth, inflation be damned. On the island of MY, they acted late, rarely, and only defensively to avoid a big depression. The government was not trying to be victor in economic contests.

On the island of E, they won their chosen battle, the one against inflation. There was essentially no inflation. There was population growth, and a little productivity growth. With these two expansions, E steadily but slowly moved along an increasing gross national product curve.

For decades, the island of E enjoyed a remarkably constant price structure. This is as well as I am able to say it to you because, after all, in time all products change, so who can be exact about what happens to prices? Even shoe leather tends to be different as a result of technological developments. Shoe manufacturing certainly does. Despite this difficulty, I can say that on the island of E there was no inflation and practically zero unemployment because there was always something to do for the government if one could land no other job. Participation in a training program to prepare for a new job was common for anyone who had lost his. That training concept was so widespread on E that it was not regarded as unemployment but merely as part of the natural portion of life's work devoted constantly to adjustment to change. Of course, the training, provided by a generally disinterested government bureaucracy, was not always beneficial.

On the island of MY there would be periodic boom times of substantial inflation and low unemployment, followed by a recession, that is, a dropping economy with substantial unemployment and deflation. Wages and prices would fluctuate and the government would let them do so, except for a rare lessening or tightening of controls on loans and credits when these looked really very badly off—say, every eight or ten years at most.

The average MY performance, as we have said, was a higher average growth rate over the decades of the late 1700s and the first decades of the 1800s than on the island of E, but there were also more severe business cycles on MY, as compared with E, of ups and downs in prices and wages, with good growth some years and poor growth in other years. The smartest people of MY generally were in private industry and the dullest in government, unlike the situation on E, although whenever it appeared that MY was in critical trouble, there would be greater temporary participation in government matters by the interested citizenry and the leadership of business and industry. On MY, there was, as compared with E, a higher average unemployment just as there was a higher average growth rate. Unlike the stable price situation of E, MY's prices doubled every twenty years, a substantial rate of inflation.

On the island of CONO, with its highest growth rate, some business cycle phenomena could constantly be observed, gains and falls of all kinds, none as severe as on MY and definitely more noticeable than with the relatively fixed economy of E. However, CONO had the highest inflation of all the islands. The constant pressure for expansion translated into very little unemployment, almost as little as on the highly controlled island of E, but the inflation was substantially higher even than on MY, just as the growth rate was higher. The combination of aggressive government action to push the economy, and the resulting competition for products, resources, and labor, all in limited supply, created a demand pull on prices that forced them up. Industry always found its costs higher from year to year for the same product because of higher wages for labor and prices for materials. Taxes to the government kept rising because it also was spending more money each year. To be profitable business had to adjust prices upward. Fortunately, the demand was there to accommodate the higher prices. The government kept enough money in circulation through modest enough requirements on bank reserves so banks could be generous in granting credit. Nearly everything produced was likely to be sold unless it was the result of bad judgment in choosing the product.

All that I have told you about CONO should have the qualification of "most of the time." CONO succeeded in avoiding totally disastrous inflation, and an overexpansion that could have exploded and caused the economy to fall apart into a disastrous depression, through government action to cut back periodically on money supply. But in the twenty years from 1820 to 1840 CONO's prices had inflated by three to one. This meant that CONO had to see that no one was harmed fatally by the inflation and might starve while the economy was growing. Specifically, the government raised government salaries such as those of teachers and those working on the water and sewage systems and in the government bank, adjusting them to go with the rising prices, though always with some lag in time that hurt those people financially. Government pensions paid to the retired were revised upward regularly, although again with a penalizing delay, so the retirees were not totally dependent upon a fixed income which could buy much less in 1840 than it could in 1820, or even 1830.

In 1820 the CONO government, as part of its money-raising for government spending, not only collected revenues by taxing everyone's income, it also sold bonds to the public, promising a reasonable interest. Many of these bonds were purchased by private citizens who expected to use the income from, and later the capital investment in, these bonds to pay for their needs when they became old. A political problem arose when it was discovered that inflation would cause these folks to have less than half of their original purchasing power in ten or fifteen years. The government worried over this.

Stopping inflation became a big issue during the 1820s. But CONO, almost as if it knew of the different experiment on E and rejected it, decided it would prefer the ills of inflation, as long as it wasn't too much inflation, to impairing economic growth. It was against their grain to take any step that seemed to have a potentially adverse effect on increasing the gross national product at the highest rate.

The leaders on CONO reasoned they could see no way to stop inflation, short of attempting such complete controls as would surely curb economic advance. As Draivio Forsa, a political candidate, said in his 1830 campaign address, "If we stop the growth, we do not produce the wherewithal to increase our overall standard of living. Surely, it is better to enjoy this increase and meet the challenge to use it wisely to provide for all so that no one will suffer and all will benefit." He defeated Conservio de Bakel who claimed that inflation had soared too high. Señor de Bakel proposed constraints on the money supply. The interest rate should be forced up, he argued, and there should be a higher requirement for bank reserves, higher taxes, and smaller government expenditures, all these actions calculated to reduce the inflationary rate to a tolerable one. He lost in a landslide.

The people of CONO in the decades from 1800 to 1840 became accustomed to a rate of inflation which would cause prices to triple in twenty years. They compared inflation, not against zero, but against what it had been the year before and the year before that. So long as inflation appeared not to be getting worse they felt they were in control of the situation. I guess they were, although I was always afraid that events would build to another panic. But they didn't, not by 1840, at any rate.

I must confess I did not learn what the limit is to which steady inflation can be tolerated while pursuing economic growth. Surely, the relation between inflation and growth is not simple. Early in the islands' history, they had enjoyed growth without inflation. Given a shortage, a pent-up demand for products that are readily producible, available resources, and plenty of labor, who would otherwise be unemployed, to do the producing, then the economy can develop rapidly to a higher gross national product figure without inflation. As production increases, if we persist in pressing for further growth with low unemployment, then inflation can arise. What is the amount of unemployment that a society should tolerate? What is the right amount of government action? It seemed that CONO was closest to it and E was furthest away from it, with MY having some of the good and bad of each. But how could I be sure? Perhaps only more time would have told me—I keep coming back to that— but my time had run out because in 1840 events of such overpowering influence took place that I had to concentrate temporarily on those rather than on further attempts to understand the workings of the isolated island economies. In 1840, the islands discovered one another and my unfinished analyses and inadequately answered questions changed to a new set.

Chapter XIV

Discovery—Then War

IN 1840, the island of CONO had over 15,000 people, and its technology had advanced to the point where it was able to build substantial sailboats that would hold several men and supplies for an ocean journey of a few hundred miles without great danger of the boats' collapsing. Engineers had built smaller and lighter versions for some years, vessels made with the new fiber glass, these plastic materials having replaced the rafts of bush bark, cotton rope, and bamboo rods previously used for one-man sailboats that moved equipment and food, and building and other materials by coastal waters around the island. (I know of no serious oversight in my planning for the California colony comparable with the failure to include seedlings for trees amongst the many items I placed on board each ship. If I had only done this, then the islands might have come together decades before and even have been able to go on to California within a few generations. But then, how could I have guessed, even if foretold of storms and ship-wrecks and fortuitously located islands, that these islands would be barren of trees?)

The boats consisted of very lightweight shells, a skeleton metal structure, covered by sheets of strong, stiff material cemented together to form solidly sealed joints that closed off and were resistant to seawater. It took only a few exploratory voyages for islanders from CONO to spot and land on the island of E, to the north, and two more months after that for them to discover also the island of MY, to the east of E.

These were not trips to foreign soil where concern about a welcome to the visitors by the natives was an issue. All three islands for a hundred years had continued imaginative speculation about the outcome of the original expedition from Spain. Had the other ships made it to California? Had they been destroyed with everyone lost during the storm? Or perhaps, as had happened to the imaginer, had his associates also landed on a friendly island somewhere?

It was members of the same "family" who were being united, speaking the same language, possessing similar forebears, and with the same dynamic experiences. For all, new worlds opened by their discovery of one anothers' existence. They were anxious to tell and hear what had happened in the last hundred years. They compared notes on every aspect of their development, the nature of their islands, their population growths, economic advances, resources, inventions, plans, and ambitions. Each island was anxious to share what it had learned with the other two.

For a few months informal barter arrangements, with much gift exchanging and loose deals for sharing products and services, took place between the islands. CONO mounted a massive shipbuilding program with promises, that is, contracts, for some of these ships to be sold to the islanders on MY and E in return for products of E and MY. It was an emergency period on CONO as the government took over the crash program, directing which product fabrication might be cut back to provide additional workers and materials for the shipbuilding, with CONO's regular needs planned to be made up partially by goods obtained from the other two islands through trade.

All were keyed up and laid plans that were far too

ambitious. The boats were small, after all. They could carry very little and it would take time to make more. So as the weeks grew to months, disappointments and letdowns now paralleled continual new excitements as each island learned of something that the other island had which it badly wanted in exchange for its own products.

The most popular pastime on all three islands became the public meetings at which travelers between islands discoursed in detail on everything that had been seen and said. Textile manufacturers, agricultural technologists, government economists, teachers, book printers, paper manufacturers, and other specialists all wanted to come together with their counterparts on the other islands to see what they possessed and knew, and how methods could be altered as a result of the discovery of the other societies after one hundred years. Talk was heard about the possibility of going on to California if only they could make ships large enough for the long voyage. But this, they knew, was far into the future.

I wish I could tell you that all continued to be peaceful, if overactive, that the islands affected one another totally beneficially, making use of their mutual existence and communication to achieve objectives more rapidly and going on to a higher social organization in which they combined resources. But alas, that is not to be the next chapter in our story. In fact, I am forced to explain how the short but important war between CONO and E came to take place, a shameful event which I could not prevent. My previously discovered ability to enter the thinking of leadership on the islands seemed to be limited by a force higher than mine. Or put it this way: when I was myself confused, when I could not see quickly enough what to coerce the leadership to do, then my influence was nil.

Part of my problem was that I did not see the war developing. Perhaps I should have. E was the island least developed technologically. It had more people than CONO and more untapped resources—minerals, rich agricultural soil, a greater variety of fish, and more pigs. CONO's aggressive industry heads soon saw the possibilities of developing E's resources. They were sincere in believing that to do so was to the benefit of both and they succeeded in selling that idea to E's government and its citizens.

The incident of the Holy Tree on E is pertinent though not necessarily the best example of the possibilities when CONO's technology was put together with E's resources. I have told you several times that the islands had no trees. Until now I have not bothered to describe what appeared to be a trivial exception. On the island of E, a narrow little peninsula led out for a few thousand feet to a small hill on which there existed only one very old, but still living, tree, presumably a relic-descendant of a period long ago when the island's environment was different. Why this last one survived, I cannot tell you. But I am able to report that the tree was an object of worship. Everyone went to contemplate it regularly. It was their living miracle and a tie to the Old World.

Regularly the scientists on E would cut small portions, from the roots to the very tip of the most distant branch, plant them, and try to produce more trees. They always failed.

Meanwhile on CONO, starting soon after the original landing in 1740, the agricultural scientists had tried again and again, always with no success, to grow taller, larger bushes—to work up from a bush to a tree. In the process, although they produced no trees, they learned a great deal about making treelike matter grow in their soil.

When the CONO agriculturalists beheld the tree on E, they hurriedly took fragments from its various portions and commenced their independent researches. In no time they began to have a small degree of success. Little trees, fertilized in ways unknown on E, began to grow on CONO. Most died very soon, the rest a little later, but it was a beginning. There was great confidence that within a few years a start might be made toward the long hoped-for forest of trees. Despite the artificial wood products created by CONO's technologists, ordinary wood was clearly superior for many applications.

Perhaps we should talk specifically of the copper mine

project. On the most southerly third of the island of E was to be found a huge body of surface copper ore of richness that could not help but interest the metal industry of CONO, particularly since CONO appeared to be running out of copper ore, or at least copper ore that was readily accessible. Together with the government of E, CONO's industry set up a plan. Through use of CONO's management, expertise, and developed equipment for mining and refining, combined with labor furnished by E, finished copper would be produced for both islands.

This copper project might have gone well except for several negative factors that arose simultaneously. First of all, this was not the only cooperative project on E. Numerous ones were begun, although individually they were smaller than the big copper project. In all of these, CONO was to supply management, advanced technology, and equipment. E would furnish the resources of the land and the labor. Not too surprisingly, now that I know what happened later, it began to be discussed on the island of E that the government had been taken in, that in actuality E had no important use for the refined copper, at least not a proper share. Similar arguments were made concerning most of the other projects. E's citizens would be working to extract and process their resources for the benefit of the citizens of CONO. Pressure began to build up for a change in the deal.

There was something else. The various understandings were worked out partially in terms of barter—specified ratios of the finished products would be delivered to each island, such as copper bowls, containers, and industrial sheets, rods, and pipe—but also partially in terms of exchange of currency of the two islands. The period of total barter had passed quickly and already currency was being exchanged before the copper deal was made final. By the time the deal was formulated a currency exchange rate had been agreed upon by both sides, using their best, fair, honest judgments as to the proper ratio between E dollars and CONO dollars. This was thought to solve the problem of different price structures on the island. A CONO dollar would buy in CONO only about one-third as much fish or shoes or agricultural products—products that were more or less comparable between the two islands—as an E dollar would buy on the island of E. (A similar beginning point of prices had once existed, we recall, based upon the first settlers' ideas of what should be approximately the price for a day's work or a fish or a pair of shoes. However, as we know, CONO had experienced much more inflation, even though their technological advance had cut down the price of many items through superior techniques of manufacture or production.)

The trouble was with CONO's inflation. E happened to have a pattern of close government direction of the economy. Its way of life included a great deal of attention to anticipating changes in prices, the value of currency and inflation or deflation, all-important to their very alert governmental response to control things rather rigidly. Initially, in setting up contracts with CONO, they were unfamiliar with the inflation situation on CONO, but as the projects advanced E began to learn about CONO's economy. In particular, E observed that CONO had experienced substantial inflation and saw that, for all practical purposes, CONO's governmental structure and industry-government-banking relationships were set up around the idea of maximum growth and the toleration of a high and steady inflation. E also noticed, to its dismay, that the new international phase of the islands' activities had caused a boom in the economy of CONO. CONO had a shortage of labor, a short supply of everything compared with the demand spurred by its ambitions, and CONO appeared to be headed for very substantial additional inflation in the period just ahead.

So E's economists began to wonder if the CONO dollars that they would receive in trade for articles and labor on the island of E would buy them very much on the island of CONO or, more especially, would buy them as much as they thought they were going to get when they made the deals. It was a huge block of their labor that they saw as being shifted over to work, in effect, for CONO, with very little to show for it.

There were social problems, too. CONO's people, being more advanced technologically and economically, and prizing such a position, felt superior to those of E. The CONO personnel on E were the managerial, skilled, professional types. They were government representatives or businessmen or bankers or engineers who were there to arrange international trade and for the transfer and use of CONO's technology. The project work on E called for lower-grade, unskilled work on the part of E. The islanders on E learned that the CONO visitors, previously friendly, stimulating, and at first so admired, looked upon E's people as backward and inferior. The resentment became deep.

The young people of E were confused and divided as to what their attitude should be toward the people of CONO who came to their island. The brilliant and self-confident CONO men who arrived to run projects captivated the young E island girls almost without trying. Some, moreover, tried and were especially successful. Their accomplishments in this area were not appreciated by E men. Of course, even the most mesmerized E girls disliked the disdainful treatment of their fathers and brothers and the haughty manner of CONO men, young and old.

Meanwhile, on CONO, their projects for exploitation of the resources of E, their huge investment, it occurred to them, might be in grave danger. They took appropriate steps.

Let me mention an interesting aside. The three islands had started their development in 1740 with their firearms know-how in precisely the same state. CONO had gone on in the development of guns, finding this the most efficient way, in the light of their other interests in metals and chemistry, to handle the killing part of the pig business. On the island of E, they used domesticating, corralling, trapping, and blows on the head. They had seen no reason to continue development or manufacture of guns. In 1840 on E, firearms were seen only in their museum. One of the steps CONO took was to equip its supervisors and managers at the copper mine and elsewhere on E with handguns.

Incidents were bound to occur. Kidding became sarcasm which became name-calling and threats which advanced to fistfights, controlled partially calmly and partially clumsily and with bias by the E police. Finally, CONO men did some shooting at E men and the island of E suddenly had a crisis on its hands. The E government held the CONO "criminals" for assault or murder. Some of the CONO suspects went into hiding. The remaining CONO visitors were directed to leave E on the available boats, never to return, and to carry the message that all trade and interaction with the island of CONO was over.

Now CONO had a crisis. No precedent existed for handling a situation of this kind. The reports were clear. CONO men seeking only to defend themselves had been tried and hanged and others were being held prisoner. Still others were being hunted down like the wild pigs. This, in response to contracts to which E was bound, which had been made in good faith and which involved such a large investment that its loss would threaten the whole economy of CONO. Its government leaders resigned in confusion and a new group took over.

Where was the island of MY in all of this? An innocent bystander, an interested observer. MY had a few people on the island of E but none of the issues they were concerned with were very important as compared with the CONO predicament. The projects between MY and CONO and MY and E were relatively small. MY's technology was not that much advanced over E nor did their inflation create a problem.

Barter with MY had also become a nuisance soon after the discoveries, of course, and MY's and E's governments agreed on an exchange rate for their currencies so trade deals could be made in either MY or E dollars. The same situation existed between MY and CONO. E's government knew MY had more inflation in their past and believed they had more likelihood of future inflation than did E. But MY's inflation was not as steady and high as CONO's. The amount of trade was small and consisted of quick sales back and forth of the special products that each had that the other would find desirable but not essential. No big projects so long in completion that inflation could alter the relative values of currency had been launched by CONO and MY. They could look at the trade balance annually, or so they thought, and adjust by revaluing or devaluing their currencies, that is, altering the exchange rate, if the imbalance in trade became troublesome.

MY had indicated an interest in obtaining some of the copper from the E-CONO project but the price had not been negotiated nor was there any hurry because the copper was not yet flowing and because MY's need for it did not appear to MY to be critical.

MY was friendly to both sides, and its citizens merely viewed with sadness the nasty situation that was developing between CONO and E. Neither CONO nor E asked MY to get into the act of their differences. There was not enough time and direct reason, and certainly no precedent for the use of a third party to settle quarrels. However, I made note of the fact that, since quarrels were inevitable amongst the three islands, they should ultimately develop some means for refereeing situations rather than reverting to bloodshed or any form of emotionally based action which would be bound to do damage to both sides.

Perhaps you see now why I could not easily conceive of something to do to prevent the war. I could not say to the brains of CONO's leadership, "Stay away! Ignore your losses!" Nor could I have said to the island of E, "Having made your deal, stick to it!" or "Stop resenting the superiority of CONO." They were not ready for that kind of thinking. It seemed that the incidents building up were inevitable as a phase of E-CONO relations. At most, I could enter into the minds of the citizens and their leadership to minimize the effect, to get the crisis over with rapidly with the least damage and to start building a more sensible relationship.

You have anticipated what happened next. CONO built a military corps of a thousand men, fifty boats, each carrying twenty soldiers with guns. They did not plan to take over the entire island of E. Even with a more modest plan they had to devote months to preparation, and the activity hurt their peacetime economy badly. People ate less and lived less well on CONO while they did everything possible to prepare their invasion force. They expanded their boat-building industry and the supportive industries required to provide all of the components and materials. They enlarged their facilities for fabricating guns. They exhausted some of their reserves of metals and chemicals. They worked every facility twenty-four hours a day and employed women and children as temporary helpers in the factories.

They decided to land on E and cut off and occupy the south third of the island which was nearest to CONO, was sparsely populated, and included the copper mine. E ran north and south and it was narrowest at about the south third point. CONO planned to land just before dawn, overpower any E islanders in the way, create a barricade across the narrow width of E just north of the mine, and prepare to fire on any of the people of E who tried to cross the line from the north.

CONO's forces carried out this invasion with complete success. It was a blitz attack. They took hostage a thousand E citizens who were south of the firing line, and announced to the island of E that they would hold that portion of the island indefinitely. They would use the hostages for labor in the mines and to cultivate the nearby fields. Other CONO citizens would arrive later. In payment for the wrongs done to the island of CONO and in recognition of CONO's investments in E, the island of E would have to accept giving up the south third of their island.

The citizens of E were stricken with fear and anger, of course. Now, I thought, was the time for me to enter the

situation. Well, almost time. A few more incidents had to occur before my recommendations could be accepted. They were quick in coming. Foolish attacks were made on the entrenched positions of the CONO force by an ad-libbed, volunteer army of E youths that acted faster than the E government could think. This courageous and naive group was not equipped to counter guns nor had they taken the time to invent a surprise plan. Of course, even if they had possessed a few rifles and great imagination, they would have failed. The plans of the CONO invasion force had been worked out very carefully. The positions they took had been well chosen; they knew the terrain. It was suicide for small E forces to attempt to take over the mine and the lost territory.

I was now able to say to the leaders of E, or rather to cause the leaders to say to the people, "Let us recognize CONO's stronger military position on our island. Let us not see thousands of our young men slaughtered. We must reason with CONO so as to make their terms lenient. Let us go to them and pledge our future cooperation. It will do them no good in the long run to hold a part of our island by force, making enemies of all our people, who outnumber theirs. We can and, if necessary, we will eventually succeed in time in driving them off the island even if it means terrible casualties for us. This they must know. If not now, then after a while, they will realize warfare is penalizing to them, too.

"Why not simply offer them all of the copper they want. We will guarantee to meet the contracts to mine and process it. There will be no more shooting and no more killing. We will recognize CONO's claims to some of the resources of the island of E."

E accepted this proposal to sue for peace (but for a hidden, additional reason, as part of a plan that was not perceived by me at the time).

Now it was the moment for me to influence the leadership of CONO. I entered the minds and used the voice of some of the most respected elders of the island who said, "Let us not fight our own brothers further. Let us forgive and forget the incidents that brought this war about. We do not want to be masters over slaves, nor do we wish to take from E what is theirs. They now realize they have wronged us, violated their contract with us. It is sensible for us to work together. We have at this moment a strong position. Let us use our strength to proceed to develop the resources of E as planned and to share in those resources. Let our superior position be our intellect, our technology, our greater efficiency in production. Let our dominance not rest in our ability to kill and take territory against the will of the people of the land."

And so the war came to an end and a new era started. It was one in which there was massive development of the technological resources of E. But I have not told you yet about something the E leadership discussed amongst themselves and to which I had not paid very much attention, so busy was I in concentrating on my words and ideas, which I wished so earnestly for them to accept.

They had a plan on E. They gave in to CONO and allowed CONO to come to E with its expertise and management skills. They agreed to cooperate by furnishing labor. They did so eagerly, cooperating in the building on the island of E an array of new and superior factories, mines, and transportation systems. Would you believe that in 1875, thirty-five years after the war, the gross national product of the previously backward island of E became greater than that of the island of CONO and the gap in favor of E began to grow rapidly? The victor in the war became so soon the loser, without realizing it until it was too late.

Chapter XV

The Ascendancy of the Economy of E; The Fall of CONO

BY 1875 the island of E had more well equipped factories and mines, and produced more boats, metal plates and containers, pipes, bottles, cloth, wheels, textile machines, tools, glass, ovens, chemicals for industry, paper, agricultural fertilizers, medicine, paper mills, and printed matter than CONO, and far more than MY. The island of E now had more technological experts, some trained many years before by the originally more advanced specialists of CONO but many more educated as youngsters in the schools and apprentice shops on E.

A large fraction of CONO's top professionals had been sent by CONO thirty-five years before, at the end of the short war, to help set up the mines and factories, guide other industrial expansion and train workers on E. Very many had remained and became full-fledged residents and citizens of E. Most of them, after over three decades on E and now in late middle age, thought of themselves as E rather than CONO men and were accepted as such, many having married E women and raised families on E with no thought of ever returning to CONO.

E's government continued to follow the pattern of the past in important respects. The government closely controlled wages and prices, the money supply and credit, and all other economic factors remotely controllable. There was essentially no unemployment. But if the E government's approach seemed the same, both before and after the war, that of the citizens was not. Here is where lay all the difference in the island world.

In the period 1840 to 1875, completely unlike the previous hundred-year history, it could no longer be said that the workers on E were unproductive with too little motivation and incentive. It is not that suddenly there was more of the flavor of free enterprise. The same determined effort persisted toward uniformity of wages within each categorization. Profits still were held in line. Entrepreneurship was inhibited if it manifested itself in promoting for too large an amount of credit at the bank and too great an expansion as judged by the government economists who still kept watch over the economy in great detail. Rather, the enormous difference was an overwhelming psychological one occasioned by the war.

E citizens had been deeply incensed by the aggressiveness, the invasion, the use of force by CONO. They had been caused to feel inferior. They knew they were technologically backward in 1840 compared with CONO. They could not even defend their land against CONO with its guns and had had to accept humiliating conditions. When they surrendered to CONO, they took a solemn pledge to each other to devote themselves to self-uplifting. Their revenge on CONO would be by quietly taking everything offered in know-how, and applying themselves diligently to surpassing CONO. This was to be the uppermost goal in life. They now had a fervor for improving their technological and economic position. All shared a clear national interest. Nothing short of

outstanding performance could satisfy them. They must out-
produce and be more advanced than CONO.

By 1880, it was apparent that it was not only E's progress
that put them far ahead. It was also CONO's decline. Because
as the 1880s opened, E was first in gross national product,
with MY second and CONO now third. E was still first in
population, with MY second, and CONO third. MY was now
first in natural resources, with E and CONO about tied
because where CONO had used more of theirs up earlier, E
was now engaged in dissipating theirs more rapidly. But of
greater interest and importance, I think, was the ranking of
the three as to the extent of government involvement in
attempts to control the economy.

I remembered the earlier ratings of several decades ago
and my quick willingness then to interpret gross national
product as suggesting, almost measuring, the worth of government direction over the affairs of the society. Back in
those early days, CONO was first, MY second, and E third in
production of goods and services, and I had judged that this
could well have been because CONO had the right amount
of government-to-private industry mix, MY had too little
action by government, and E had too much. But now E was
first in both its economic success and its tightness of governmental control. MY was still in the middle, with its weak and
scarcely noticeable government action, while CONO, previously having the right amount of government partnership,
with strong free enterprise, not too much and not too little,
was now at the very bottom in gross national product. It had
to be doing something wrong, I reasoned.

Apparently, a unanimously determined citizenry, agree-
ing on the national interest, devotedly committed to the
attainment of a goal, could transcend the evils and handicaps
of its system. I said this to myself but I really did not completely buy it. True, the government on E was well inten-
tioned. It set government priorities, did realistic planning,
knew that not everything could be done at once, and per-

formed analyses continually to compare alternatives for assignment of resources and manpower, seeking the courses which might best fit the goals. But its overregulation, its interfering with motivation had to be costly. Government bureaucracy could use up man-hours that should instead be applied to turning out higher production.

On the other hand, big swings in the economy are costly, too, I had to admit, and E avoided those. Work not done during a period of unemployment, higher costs to produce when there is low volume—these losses are never again recovered. If it were possible to arrange, it would be better to avoid the big economic swings by taking the right actions. CONO took actions, but rarely right, usually late, often in the wrong direction. MY took little action at all and let the ups and downs in the economy just go their own way and dissipate, and MY's economy succeeded better than CONO's. Apparently, a very minimum of action by government, while not as good as the best action, is better than a large amount of pushing in the wrong direction.

CONO's decline, its loss of character, made it easier for E to succeed. Far from pursuing mastery of E after the war, CONO citizens began to luxuriate in the production now coming from E. As E provided CONO with much of what it needed, CONO's output fell off. A master-slave relationship existed in a peculiar way and worked reverse havoc. CONO's citizens, convinced of their superiority, began automatically to accept the idea that E citizens should work hard and provide the necessities for the people of CONO, the aristocrats and masters.

CONO became lazy and inefficient and the manpower required to produce, distribute, or maintain anything, or render any service, rose rapidly on CONO. So prices soared. When the government, concerned by increasing inflation, tried to curb the expansion of the money supply by tightening credit, the voters would not have it. They wanted to buy homes and most other things on credit, confident the price would be higher if they waited until later when they had the money. They also demanded a broadening ensemble of government services provided to them, more than they would or could pay for in taxes. The government printed the extra money required to make up the difference, creating a deficit, year after year, between government income and expenditures. The government demand was added to the consumer and industry demand, increasing the inflation. The supply of CONO-made products and services was not going up, although their cost was.

With prices rising it was no surprise to find workers demanding—on threat of strikes which would halt production and even essential government services—increases in pay to keep their buying power from eroding. Certainly no government could be elected that denied most people the hope of rising income so as at least to equal the increasing prices. But with productivity decreasing, CONO was producing less per person each year, not more. The government was powerless to do anything but give in, allow inflation to take its course, and keep up the budget deficits.

The workings of the inflationary spiral on CONO were both painful and fascinating to watch. For instance, take the general increase in wages at one point in 1845. I am not saying now whether it was unjustified or justified, this depending upon whether one is the person working and about to receive the increase, or an employer who has to pay it, or a government official who has to be for it to get elected and against it as the consequences arrive later. Almost immediately after the wage increase had taken place, consumer demand rose because the wage earners were also consumers. Credit was available so the consumer not only bought with cash but on credit, a good many of the credit purchasers believing they were going to get further wage raises and thus would be able to pay when required to later.

This buying led to several things, although there was a little time delay. In the general inflationary climate everyone assumed he had better buy now for the future, whether he was a buyer at retail of something for his own use, a wholesaler or distributor considering what orders to place at the factories, or a factory manager considering commitments for equipment and materials for future delivery. Interest rates rose as everyone competed for credit from the available money supply.

Now, from previous deliberations I already know that compensatory effects should set in. Eventually at the new high prices and high interest rates, the buying and borrowing would slow down and inventories on CONO would rise. Distributors would start to fire employees. I could see some of these compensations setting in by 1846, a year after the wage increase. But there was interference with the free market by the CONO government.

There was the case of Ricardo Semiloco, whose company took on a contract in 1845 to build the new sewer system on CONO, the first one really to cover the entire island. This contract was the result of competitive bidding amongst a number of large companies who wanted to do the job for the government. The Semiloco Company won the award by underbidding badly, gambling they could later get a revision to their guarantee to perform the task on a fixed price. Anxious to win the award, they had ignored the evidence of continuing inflation. The job was a three-year project. During this period costs increased by over 30 percent owing to wage increases and increases in the cost of materials. Moreover, they had been optimistic in figuring basic labor costs to the extent of 40 percent. To make matters worse, they had also ignored certain technical difficulties—they had planned to dig some tunnels through hills in a number of places to effect downhill flow into the ocean and had underestimated the task of getting through the hard terrain. These problems increased costs 50 percent.

The result was that the Semiloco Company was in grave financial difficulties in 1846 and could not remotely complete the job it had undertaken for the price that had been agreed upon. If it went broke and fired its employees, the consequences would be unacceptable socially and politically

because of the effect on the economy, specifically on the employment picture. Moreover, the island needed the new sewers.

Any of several courses of action could have been taken. But the one that the CONO government chose was simply to have the government lend money to the company sufficient to see them through the project. The work was completed and employment was maintained during that period by the Semiloco Company. They ended up with an enormous debt which they never could pay off, the government had a larger accumulated deficit, and CONO's inflation was encouraged.

More often than not, the action of CONO's government made the inflation worse and even accentuated the negatives of the ordinary economic swings. At times of peak employment, relatively high production by private industry, and general optimism, the government would take advantage of the optimistic business environment to catch up on delayed and needed private works, such as roads, bridges, sewers, schools, bank buildings, and improved harbors. Its spending would accelerate the upswing, what with the government out competing for relatively scarce labor and materials.

With any falling off of economic activity and increasing unemployment, the government would cut its projects, thinking they could not be afforded. So the government's spending slowed down just when the general spending did, adding to the dip in the economic cycle. The cry for economy in government also very often would force the government to lay off some of those providing government-furnished services, adding to the unemployment.

I have often inveighed against the controlled economy of E. However, I admit they were at least trying to synchronize these matters a bit. Government projects on E were started, not stopped, during slack periods. CONO, however, could never quite decide between being a free enterprise economy, with a minimum of government intervention, and bringing the government into action to plan and control to a greater extent. They tended to get the worst of both worlds. They had lots of government intervention but not the right kind or at the right time, not well planned but rather in response to emotional demands of the voters after a crisis already had established itself.

It became habitual on CONO for government spending to exceed its income. Year after year large government budget deficits built up. What the government was doing largely was printing money to pay for its expenditures that were beyond its income, adding to the money supply and increasing the inflationary pressure. The government did have and did use another source to fund these deficits. It sold bonds to the public and to the banks, which is a way of saying that it borrowed money. The government bonds were, of course, simply IOUs by the government to those who bought them, promising to pay them back at a later time with interest. With so many bonds outstanding, the government had an annual interest expense to add to its other expenditures, thus making its deficit even worse.

Now, I don't mean to suggest that when CONO operated with a government budget deficit, this was always a certain and major contributor to their steady inflation. In an economic downturn, deficit government spending could neutralize deflation and provide impetus to economic recovery and growth. A downturn is characterized by substantial unemployment and a completely ample capacity to provide goods for sale, but too little purchasing power. The added money put into the system by government expenditures under such circumstances should help to increase the demand relative to supply without prices rising very much, if at all. The government deficit could be looked upon as merely a way of shifting people from the status of unemployed to a status of doing something useful for the society, such as distributing, shipping, selling, and maintaining equipment and goods that would be bought and used rather than simply

resting in the warehouses and gathering dust while the unemployed sat around gathering unemployment relief
payments.

My considered belief about the effect of government
spending on inflation, having watched CONO long and hard,
is that it is either important or unimportant, good or bad,
depending upon how far away the economy is from a full-
employment economy. Full employment, I think of as when
unemployment is not excessive, not the unattainable ideal of
zero either, but small. When unemployment is low and the
government nevertheless goes ahead and spends more money
than it takes in, then inflation can be expected from such
action and it should be avoided. CONO did not do such
avoiding in the years after the war. In the second half of the
1800s CONO was too often. distinguished by having full
employment but with poor productivity, too many of the
workers lazy and having a casual attitude toward the quality
of the product they were producing. With prices rising and
pressure to get the wages up to keep purchasing power constant, about all that was needed in addition to cause inflation
to soar was for the government to go on a spending spree.

Labor unions, if one uses those words to cover even the
most informal organization of workers to militate for rights
or advantages for the workers, existed on all three islands
within a decade or so after the landings. A hundred years
later, however, labor unions as major factors in the economy,
were important only on the island of CONO. On E, the very
tight control by government over wages, training, location
and relocation of workers, and many of the other aspects of
economic growth and job opportunity that might result from
such growth, made labor unions a minor activity. At best, the
labor unions on E were "town meetings," forums for workers
to present their views to one another. Sometimes the participants influenced government leaders in attendance or those
who were told later of the recommendations formulated, but
most often they came just to hear themselves speak and
complain. The organizations tended to be social clubs with a

substantial portion of their activity going into intracompany athletic events.

On the island of MY labor unions were not very important because there were few large companies and many family-owned small businesses in which the workers were relatives of the owners. There were employee-employer squabbles but they were not the kind in which a union of workers would have very much bearing on the matter. Besides, on MY the independence people showed in attitudes toward government bureaucracy was manifested also by a general antipathy toward any organizations with rules and regulations, and labor unions were well endowed with these.

On CONO, however, where there were many large companies, large and formal organizations of workers were formed, seeking aggressively to press for the interests of the workers. Labor unions were a factor in political elections on CONO, even as was big business. Part of the atmosphere of ups and downs in the economy and of in-and-out government involvement in attempts to control economic evils or assist economic growth resulted from the contests among and the strength of the many special-interest groups, be they consumers, workers, managers, owners, bankers, politicians, or professional groups. Many were members of several such groups. Everyone was a consumer and many shifted in and out of government, business, industry, education, and labor.

When the organized workers received wage increases, it became common on CONO to set up contracts between the workers' groups and the managers of business and industry. Most of these deals promised future wage increases to preserve the purchasing power of the workers against inflation. A typical agreement would say that in the following year, if it turned out there was a given percent inflation in living costs, then the wages would be increased by that same percentage.

CONO's government, business leaders, workers, and general public all expected further inflation. It was felt also that the economy would be dealt a disastrous blow if the typical citizen did not receive wage increases that would enable him to go on buying the article produced. It was reasonable to expect he should be paid more if everything he had to buy should rise in price. One thing guaranteed the other, of course. Each following year there was a wage increase because prices had indeed risen. Equally, there was certain to be a price increase because cost of wages had increased earlier. The government found itself powerless to interfere with this automatic escalation and the permanent inflation which had to be its consequence.

CONO, reconciled to permanent inflation, even tried to arrive at a fixed, acceptable annual inflation. One government leader, Optimas del Supresio, at one time made a considerable political effort based on a proposal that at Christmastime each year all prices, wages, deposits in the bank, loans and savings, taxes, and government pensions should be automatically increased by 10 percent. Of course, he asked that there be a voluntary deferment of all increases during the rest of the year. He felt this 10 percent would suffice. It was near the average figure of the several years before. It had somehow been lived with so 10 percent could not be said to be a disturbingly high figure. Moreover, as Supresio said, "Why should inflation worry us? If all numbers inflate in unison, no one will lose his purchasing power, the value of his investment or his savings." We only find inflation difficult to live with, he claimed, if things inflate in disharmony, not harmony—one person's salary going up, another person's savings or pension going down.

His system was never tried. His opponent, Remundo Re Alite, won the citizens' vote by hammering away steadily at the point that if everyone could be forced to hold off inflation until Christmas then they could just as well hold back forever, since as Supresio had said, nothing is changed by a uniform, universal inflation. It was fate that CONO did not know how to control inflation, whether to make it uniform or to make it zero or small.

The inflation on CONO, of course, aggravated—more accurately, it accelerated—the transfer of production to E

because even for most products in which the factories of
CONO still were in active operation and competition, their
prices were higher in CONO dollars than the price of similar
E products. This was true even though the latter were
brought across hundreds of miles of ocean.

The CONO developments I described began to be apparent to me by 1855 and were totally visible by 1860. I
began to be concerned about the system of international
money exchange because it was not clear how long CONO
could go on printing CONO dollars and purchasing E products with those dollars. "What," I began to ask myself, "will
E do with all of this paper money, the surplus CONO dollars
it is collecting and not returning to CONO for CONO-made
products?" We shall return to this issue, the one of imbalance
of payments between CONO and E, in a short while. First,
however, we must see the effect of the island of MY in all of
this.

MY, having not been involved in the war in any way,
was aloof from and quite independent of the forced postwar
arrangements between CONO and E. On the other hand,
they participated to a substantial extent in the transfer of
technology out of CONO. Many small projects began to have
a cumulative and powerful effect over a period of years. Like
E, the island of MY vastly improved its technology in the
decades of the 1840s and 1850s based upon the beginnings it
was able to obtain from CONO. But the island of MY was
able to exact its own terms without running into difficulty
with CONO. It did this by shrewdness in trade negotiations
and by exploiting CONO's experience with E. CONO did
not want trouble in trade with MY, and MY was careful in
the 1840s to ask for conditions that appeared reasonable and
attractive to CONO.

On MY, free enterprise was especially pronounced and
individual MY entrepreneurs sought out independent deals
with their counterparts on the island of CONO, carefully
analyzing both the market on CONO and their own domestic
market for each of their specialized products. For example,

the island of MY noticed the superior techniques used on CONO with regard to the treating of food products to make them last longer—the smoking of fish and meat, the preserving of seed and grain, the sealing of substances in bottles and cans. By arrangements with business and industry on CONO, MY entrepreneurs applied these techniques to their specialty food products. Certain fish, birds, and fruit around the island of MY were rare on the other two islands and the people on CONO and E found them especially appetizing.

Similarly, factories on the island of MY found they could sell to the luxury-minded citizens of CONO unique MY products such as clocks and lamps for the home, and cloth of interesting texture and design. With artistry, individual initiative, and creativity at its maximum on the island of MY, and with the government offering no handicaps, MY citizens were at once highly imaginative and bold and, in the business sense, very clever in what they chose to do. MY's nearly totally individual, private enterprise system began to blossom in the second half of the 1800s, and MY began to enjoy great prosperity, developing their resources fully and organizing efficient distribution methods. MY used the free market forces skillfully so as to produce what the market really wanted and reaped the profit rewards.

Of great importance is the fact that the private bankers of the island of MY succeeded in making some deals for the transfer of products to CONO which involved MY having the right to bring CONO dollars to the CONO government bank and receive gold in exchange. Now this may appear to you to be a remarkable and surprising achievement, and indeed it was. How could the government of CONO have allowed itself to distribute any of the gold which it alone possessed to either of the other two islands? By what kind of carelessness by CONO, or response to a breakthrough in salesmanship or reasoning by MY, did CONO permit gold to leave the island and come into possession of residents of MY when CONO had for so long made it illegal for its own residents to possess gold?

This brings us to the whole subject of how, when the islands traded with one another, they were able to make payments in their respective currencies. How did they arrange relationships, that is, exchange rates, between their currencies? I have already spoken of the difficulties in this respect that, in part, brought on the war. I refer to the inflation on CONO and the consequent inability of the islanders of E to believe that deals which they made with CONO on exchange rates between currencies were going to continue satisfactorily in view of that inflation. With the high degree of production on E and with so much of it going to inflation-plagued CONO for CONO's use, how could a stable trade payment situation be maintained? And how did CONO's gold supply figure in all of this?

Chapter XVI

The International Money Crisis

AFTER THE WAR, each nation had gone on receiving and accepting the other nations' currency in exchange for goods. Most often, however, it was CONO dollars that were used. When someone on the island of MY sold goods to someone on the island of CONO, the price was set in CONO dollars, and the same was true of trade between E and MY and between E and CONO. On each island, they used their own dollars, paying their workers and keeping their domestic accounts in their own currency as they had always done. But the government and private banks kept a supply of currency of all three islands and held funds on deposit for traders on each. Typically, a metals producer on E, for example, would have bank accounts on CONO and MY as well as on the island of E, its home state. This is because it would be making sales and receiving payments on each of the islands. It might even be paying charges for distribution, ocean voyage fees, and commissions locally in the local currencies. International banking was more than an important adjunct to international trade. It was an essential aspect thereof.

Now, why were CONO dollars the international currency, the most commonly used monetary units? One reason was a natural one. CONO did more buying, more importing, from the other islands, and it paid in CONO dollars. It was on balance (perhaps I should say "imbalance"), importing goods and exporting CONO dollars more than it was exporting products and obtaining CONO dollars back in payment. CONO was also investing heavily in E facilities, at least in the 1840s and '50s. Its "balance of payment" of international currency exchange was negative.

Another reason was the insistence by CONO on the use of its dollars just after the war when its economic and military strength were highest as was also its business aggressiveness. CONO dollars should be the standard, for many reasons, CONO had argued. CONO was putting up the initial investments for joint operations on the other two islands. It was not the other way. CONO, with the greatest wealth, the largest purchasing power, as well as the largest production, would be making the major purchases, placing its currency in the hands of the other two islands, and not the other way about. CONO wanted CONO dollars to be used, because it identified that with keeping financial control—only CONO could print CONO dollars. It felt that, as the richest, most powerful economic entity of the three, its dollars should be the "standard" and the other two currencies should be subservient.

The posture of CONO in 1840 was overwhelmingly strong compared with both E and MY. Everyone accepted as the important feature of international trade that CONO was exporting its more advanced know-how to help the other two islands catch up. CONO, to assist this process, made heavy investment of CONO dollars (largely in E, as in the ill-fated copper mine) and made loans to the governments of E and MY in CONO dollars. Individuals and private businesses on CONO made loans to individuals and businesses on the other two islands. The longer-term idea was that after the more backward islands built up their businesses and industry and commenced to produce goods of value, the goods would be sold at a profit and the CONO investment would be paid back. So, for the first decade after the war, it was not surprising that more CONO dollars, many more, were in the hands of the islanders of E and MY and their governments and private banks than there were E and MY dollars on CONO.

Everyone assumed, especially the leadership of CONO, that the production and economies of E and MY would advance rapidly and there would be ample justification for expanding the supply of CONO dollars. They would have told us that the excess CONO dollars printed, and the investment made by and the credit extended from CONO, represented new facilities created on E and MY that would later produce more goods. This was not dangerous inflation, they believed. This was sound investment by a wealthy nation in a lesser-developed nation and thus it was good business for both nations. Why worry that the flow of CONO dollars was from CONO to E and would be "imbalanced" in this sense for years? Eventually, each CONO dollar sent to E would create several CONO dollars flowing back, representing a healthy, though delayed, return on the investment. It was prudent use of an expanding money supply to go with an expanding economy. If the CONO dollars had to be translated on E and MY into the currencies of these islands in order to pay the workers associated with the expanding facilities there, then this was perfectly all right. A printing up of E dollars and MY dollars by E and MY of approximately the right amount would be accomplished by their government banks for local use, and there need be no cause for alarm, it was thought. A business on E that received CONO dollars for something it produced and sent to CONO would simply deposit them in the E bank and receive on demand the equivalent in E dollars to pay its workers. The E banker would take the CONO dollars to the E government bank where E dollars were printed as required to make the exchange. The problem of a piling up of excess CONO dollars, if that happened, was thus a problem for the E government bank and not for the private businesses of E.

All three islands' people had a very healthy interest in these economic matters, going back, I trust, to my initial indoctrination of all of their forefathers. Also, they retained vivid memories of the great depressions some decades ago. In 1840, when economists from E, CONO, and MY came together for the first time, they were most interested in learning that a runaway instability had been experienced everywhere and was regarded as repeatable unless careful government examination of the money supply took place, although they differed as to the extent to which the government must watch and control every aspect of the economy.

Thus, it was not surprising that general concern existed about exchanging separate currencies, one for the other, by any fixed ratio. Trying to keep the economies in even, side-by-side, parallel operation looked improbable when the three autonomous islands could independently print their currency, extend bank credit, influence their island's money supply and, with it, inflation and economic growth. Make no mistake about it, the islanders were excited by the new economic growth that their discovery of each other and the spreading of the advanced technology of CONO could bring them all. But there were economic specialists who worried and whose concerns influenced the governments and the business and labor groups of all the islands. CONO's inflation certainly was seen to be excessive by some on E and, for that matter, even by the leadership of MY though they had less potential losses to ponder.

Pressure existed to find some way to make the exchange of goods by the use of three diverse money systems practical, controllable, and unlikely to cause trouble. The economies were being uplifted and people were busy with their activities, working, making money, or risking investment, but the concern was there.

On CONO, a special worry accompanied the use of the CONO dollar as the international currency. From CONO's standpoint, they had the burden of major investment at risk.

CONO was building the economies of the other two islands by exporting its wealth and advanced know-how. Some on CONO argued it should keep the money and the knowledge to itself, that the sharing and investing would bring it nothing but grief. Was not one war enough? Others said that even if war was ruled out, and this rejection was the popular idea, what assurance was there that the transfer of technology would pay off? Could not all of the investment of funds from CONO to develop industry on the other two islands be lost in a government take-over the moment there was an unfriendly or overly competitive environment on the other islands? Particularly, of course, they were concerned about the island of E, where the biggest transfer of funds and capability had been made.

It occurred to them that they should make some concessions if it would guarantee that the CONO dollar would dominate economic exchange, the pricing structure, the contracts between nations, the vehicle for straightening out accounts and making international financial transfers between nations and individuals. CONO controlled no aspect of the E or MY economies. As long as the CONO dollar, which they did control, was the currency of international exchange, they felt safer.

I began to understand for the first time that there was a big difference in the impact of unsolved inflation for a domestic economy in isolation as compared with an international environment. When CONO was alone it was able to override for a long time the ills of inflation somewhat through religious fervor for advancing technology and economic growth. Rampant inflation, where everyone comes to expect that a dollar will buy less next year, can seriously hurt investment for growth without which the growth won't happen. Where wages go up in line with productivity increases and not through inflation, the consumer is able to buy the increased output. Then investments in greater capacity produce a return on that investment more or less in accordance with expectancy. But when prices are rising rapidly, labor is panicky and insistent on getting wages high enough to retain purchasing power as prices rise. Then there is a profit-squeeze in industry as its costs escalate, the government is in the act trying to curb inflation, everyone becomes fearful of what is going to happen next, and the environment for investment deteriorates and motivation disappears. Unemployment can exist during continued inflation and production resources are not used in the most sensible way. The government is forced to spend more for unemployment relief and to tax more to raise the funds to do so, and the standard of living does not go up.

It is not really possible to have inflation out of control and still get economic growth in the long run. But substantial economic growth and substantial inflation can coexist for years. This CONO demonstrated.

CONO, with its constant inflation, had been heading for a period when its economic growth would slow drastically, I now realized. If there had been no discovery of the other islands, CONO would have found its inflation too penalizing for further growth eventually. With its fortuitous technological advance, which increased productivity rapidly, CONO had been able for decades to enjoy economic advance even as inflation was eroding the foundation of that advance. But now all of this had caught up with CONO. After the war it needed only the presence of E's low-labor production build-up for CONO's economy to suffer the deterioration that it had been heading toward for a long time.

What could stabilize the CONO dollar, give everyone confidence, and cause the CONO dollar to be supreme? CONO's leadership knew they could not attain or guarantee a zero or even a small inflation. They had been fighting inflation for years and the present circumstances, if anything, seemed to be further overheating the economy. By 1850, as these problems were developing, all the negative conditions I described earlier as having blossomed out on CONO to their fullest by 1875 were quite apparent. CONO had permanent, incurable, chronic inflation. Labor unions, in response to

inflation on CONO, were succeeding with the actuality and
the threat of strikes in bringing wages up. If the government
tried to hold prices firm despite the resulting rising labor
costs, it would mean less profit for business. Less profit would
mean less taxes to cover the government expenditures the
citizens insisted not be cut, and it would mean that private
business would be less inclined to make new investments.
CONO was committed now to the expanding international
economy. A collapse of all of its plans for major investment
in E would mean a collapse of the government on CONO
and a massive economic disaster.

The government of CONO was on the horns of a dilemma and the leadership of CONO outside of government
also recognized it. They had to accept high inflation and their
only hope was to get it down a bit. They further had to
accept the evidence of decreasing productivity on the part of
their workers, that their way of life was changing, that it was
going to be exceedingly difficult to assure a stable economy.
They went all out to invest in further economic expansion
on the international front, seeing this, though not clearly, as
a way to continue to advance economically, trading their
know-how for production of products for their economy.

Precisely this pattern on CONO was observed by the
leadership of E and MY. Worry increased about acceptance
and use of CONO dollars, whose value might go down in real
purchasing power substantially compared with their own
currencies in the course of one year, that is, in less time than
the completion of some projects which had been based upon
fixed-price contracts.

The government banks of E, CONO, and MY tried to
use agreed-upon exchange ratios for each combination of
pairs of currencies. All that was needed, when it was seen
that CONO tolerated more inflation than did E, for example,
was for E and CONO to meet and agree to implement a new
ratio to compensate for the inflation. It was simple in principle. In practice, there were problems. Gambling on the
occurrence of a ratio change in the future became natural

and common. Private banks, businesses, and individuals engaged in this speculative game. Governments could not stop
the gambling. Even controlling it was difficult. For instance,
if someone on CONO who had the financial means to do so
decided that in a few months an E dollar would bring more
CONO dollars in exchange than at the present moment, he
could convert all of his CONO dollar holdings into E dollars ahead of time by going to the CONO central bank and
asking for the exchange. He might even borrow CONO dollars to engage in this kind of speculation. Of course, the
government banks assumed the important role of trying to
anticipate these changes themselves for these central banks
were not there for the prime purpose of conveniently aiding
private speculators to get rich. Rather, they were trying to
maintain realistic ratios of currency exchange so that trade
could be fostered in the interest of the nations on each side
of the exchange. With powerful nongovernment businesses
and individuals investing large funds in risk-taking or changes
of currencies (trying to anticipate changes in exchange ratios
ahead of government action for private profit-taking) the
maintenance of official ratios was made more difficult. The
influential speculators indirectly pressured the governments
to act so as to confirm and support the gambling position
taken.

It was always hoped that E would buy as much from
CONO as CONO from E, on the average, over a period of
time. Then neither bank would accumulate too many dollars
of the other's currency and have no need to question the
agreed-upon exchange ratio. Such a neat balance in payments
would be evidence that buyers and sellers were satisfied with
the prices they worked out in the respective currencies.
If the E central bank found it was acquiring too many CONO
dollars it could go to CONO's central government bank and
change them for CONO's E dollars. But it could do so only
if CONO had enough E dollars to make the exchange. Unfortunately again and again CONO's supply of E dollars
would run out. CONO seemed unable to build up a reserve

of E dollars because CONO simply was not selling enough to
E. So, periodically, E would unilaterally announce a change
in the ratio, hoping to curb the one-sided flow. This meant
that anyone on E who was sending an exported item out to
CONO would now receive more CONO dollars in payment,
which is to say that the price of the E product on CONO
would become higher. Presumably, CONO would not want
to buy so much at the higher prices and this should have
caused a smaller number of CONO dollars to come to E and
find themselves in E's government bank. Conversely, CONO's
products should now look more attractive, that is, cheaper,
to customers on E. Thus, E should buy more from CONO
and CONO's banks should begin to acquire more E dollars
which they could use to trade off against CONO dollars.
Then neither central bank on either of the two islands should
find itself with an embarrassing buildup of paper from the
other country.

But it did not work quite this way. Recall that E had
that habit and commitment to high and steady production.
The E people liked things to go according to plan and they
hated adjusting to unforeseen and sudden ups and downs. A
factory manager on E, having scheduled to produce a certain
amount of goods and sell half of it to CONO, was quite happy
to receive the CONO dollars, take them to the E government
bank and get E dollars for them, using these to pay for his
materials and labor. If all over the island of E a large fraction
of E's goods produced were sent to CONO and the E central
government bank was storing too large a surplus of CONO
dollars, that was the government bank's problem, not his.
True, it was a frequent discussion topic on E that E's people
were working hard and helping to produce CONO's needs
with little to show for it. Nevertheless, the factory manager
and most of the workers put that issue way back in their
minds when they were engaged in production scheduling and
marketing. Their overriding interest was steady work and
continued growth in production. If concerned about anything, it was the possibility that a monetary revaluation by E

might cause CONO to cancel some of its orders for their production, leaving them with unpleasant cutbacks and unemployment.

Every time E's government raised its products' prices on CONO (by changing the ratio of CONO dollars required in exchange for an E dollar) CONO and E buyers and sellers managed adjustments and the imbalance in dollar shifts continued. The primary and distressing counter was by CONO's buyers who simply paid the higher price, though buying at a lower quantity level, inflating the price structure on CONO some more, and leaving the CONO dollar flow to E unchanged. The CONO government policies and actions encouraged this additional price inflation and its attendant wage inflation in a helpless submission to the CONO people's inadvertently foolish inflationary pressure.

Too many CONO dollars in the central bank on E was a serious worry for E's government. Every time a producer on E exported to CONO, received CONO dollars, and asked for E dollars in return at the E central bank so he could pay his workers, the government of E had to authorize the printing of more E dollars to meet the requirement. Thus E could not control its printing of E dollars, this printing being tied to CONO dollars coming in. Looking ahead, the government realized it had to find an answer to the problem of this imbalance of currency exchange. The matter was confused somewhat by the realization that so long as production of all of the islands was increasing and international trade was going up even more rapidly than domestic growth on each island, with the islands becoming more dependent on one another's products, there would have to be more money in international circulation. CONO dollars were the main medium of international exchange. Thus one would expect everyone to hold more CONO dollars as time passed just to keep the magnitude of the trade operations everywhere increasing. But the island of E was storing up more CONO dollars than would be represented by its requirement for money in circulation and a reserve for future purchases. So by 1850, E had had unilaterally to revalue the CONO-to-E-dollar relationship several times. For all practical purposes, there were no fixed currency exchange rates. The "fixed" rates became "unfixed" too often. Whether E liked it or not, international trade with CONO meant living with a severe handicap to E's determination to control its own money supply. E had to tolerate the existence of gamblers and speculators who tried to anticipate future currency ratios. Its own economy was dependent on another island's economy over which it had no control. E had to plan on being unable to plan well, as it used to when it was an isolated nation. Optimum use of its resources, human and physical, and economic growth and a minimum of dislocation to its economy from factors not under its control all appeared to be threatened.

It was way back in 1850, as I saw this international trade imbalance forming, that it occurred to me to put an ingenious thought into the minds of the leadership of the islands. I would have them consider that the answer to all international monetary problems was to adopt the gold standard universally for all three islands.

Considering that only CONO had gold, it might occur to you that this was a preposterous suggestion. But bear me out. Forgetting practicality for only a moment, my plan can be seen to have possessed a rather simple rationale. Let the widely used and held CONO dollars be genuinely backed up by gold on CONO. A CONO dollar could be turned in to the CONO government bank and a specified amount of gold would be handed out in return on demand. Then we would set a ratio, that is, an exchange rate of an E dollar and a MY dollar to a CONO dollar that all banks and businesses would honor. A business on E could take its E dollars to a bank and demand and receive the right number of CONO dollars if it wanted CONO dollars. Or a bank on any island could take CONO dollars to the government central bank in CONO and demand E or MY dollars or else gold for the CONO dollars.

Again putting aside practicality for a further instant, we

see that so long as everyone could get gold on demand and, presumably, was quite willing to possess gold instead of currency, then any concern at any time about currency would be resolved by simply buying gold with it. If CONO tended to overprint CONO currency and holders of it had any worry about it they would, presumably, always rush to convert their CONO dollars, as soon as they received some, into gold. The only reason why anyone then would care about exchange rates and inflation of economies on one or another island would be because of a fear he might be unable to trade a specific currency for gold quickly enough, before the gold was used up or denied him. With a universal gold standard, the only problem would be whether the universal gold standard would be certain, lasting, respected, and adhered to—at least long enough to get to the bank. So now we must face the question of practicality. Is there any chance at all that the gold standard idea could work in practice and, if so, how could it be brought about?

Please be assured that I recognized the proposal would be summarily rejected at first. This was one reason I had the island of MY make the proposal rather than E. MY was less tied up in interactions with CONO's economy, had many fewer CONO dollars coming in and much less overall CONO influence on its island. It could act a bit as an independent referee, although not entirely.

Of course, CONO immediately replied to MY's proposal that it was fantastically silly. That much gold did not exist in CONO's vaults. The total amount of CONO dollars in circulation vastly exceeded the value of gold in the treasury of CONO that was supposed to back them up. CONO, except once, nearly a century ago, on a purely temporary and probably erroneous basis, had never let its gold leave its treasury, not even to its own citizens, they pointed out. But I supplied MY with a counterargument.

"Of course," said MY's principal economist to his counterpart in CONO, "you do not have enough gold. But who is talking about everyone converting all of his CONO dollars into gold? What would we all do with that much gold? We all need the CONO dollars to carry on our trade. You have found on CONO for over one hundred years that, short of a great economic collapse, no one really comes to the bank to demand gold—except perhaps a very small amount. Just as you have not needed a quantity of gold comparable with the dollars in currency and deposits outstanding to have a satisfactory money system based on gold, neither will the three islands need a gold supply comparable with the total CONO dollars in circulation. You have enough gold. You simply have now to share it properly amongst the three islands. If you do not, we shall not have real stability in the use of CONO dollars as a principal currency."

Now I must tell you that I had another reason for this suggestion and, more particularly, another reason for having MY make the proposal. By this time, 1850, I had already decided that it did not make very much difference what standard supposedly lay behind the currency. What was important was the way the money was regarded by the citizens and the government, how its supply was controlled, what happened to government spending and bank credit and taxes, and hence inflation. But I knew that the gold standard had great psychological force on all three islands. Certainly it did on CONO. Here and there could be found skeptics like me, but most people equated the existence of a gold standard with monetary strength, reserves, and stability. While E and MY had gotten along without gold, it had always had a magical significance for them, if for no other reason than that it had been handed down to them by their fathers that gold had been important in the old mainland world. Gold was real money, not paper money.

But this was not the big reason I had that I am trying to get around to telling you about. I regarded it as bad that CONO's currency had emerged as the practical world trade currency. It was CONO that was in least control of its money supply, that was inflating more rapidly than the other two islands. That is like letting the man with the shakiest hands carry the explosive.

I felt that if CONO had an obligation to give up some of its gold on demand, which I knew it would be very, very reluctant to do, it might mend its ways. CONO then would have the motivation to control its monetary system, its whole economic plan, its international ambitions, its economic expansion, as to minimize inflation. What ought to happen, I argued, is that about as many dollars and as much goods valued in dollars should be exported from an island as came in. The island of E, for example, could come to have a surplus of CONO dollars, only as a result of selling a great deal to CONO and buying very little in return I could understand CONO's investing heavily in building up in the 1840s. Wise investments and loans from CONO to E would in time enable E to produce wealth to repay the loans and generate a good future return on the investment. Such CONO dollars would be used by E to buy equipment and services from CONO as part of the natural development of a weaker state by a friendly, stronger one. However, CONO could not expect long-term cooperation with its neighboring islands if its workers did not work, and CONO simply printed money in exchange for everything they needed produced by the hard work of nearby islanders.

As I was going through these deliberations in 1850, CONO required some $25 million a year worth of food, clothing, machinery, seeds, and every other kind of materiel. The only sensible way to succeed in getting the other islands to furnish a good fraction of what CONO needed would be to do something for them of about equal value in return. How could I drive that point home? How could I force on CONO the realization of this and the mass determination to do something about it? One answer, I thought, would be to discipline them with the threat of the loss of their gold. Gold would be something acceptable that they could trade to the other islands in return for whatever the other islands were going to furnish to them, at least until they were threatened with running out of gold. Then they would have to revalue CONO dollars to where everyone was willing to hold them and not trade them for gold. If the CONO dollar thus were lowered enough, the trade balances would work out. People on the other islands would then perhaps be interested in buying CONO products in exchange for theirs and the international trade situation would stabilize.

When MY pressed this proposal for a gold standard, what with the rather modest surplus of CONO dollars MY was accumulating, CONO could consider the proposal more objectively than if faced with a similar proposal by E. However, they knew they could not really do something in their economic relationship with MY very different from what they were doing with E. If they allowed MY to obtain gold for CONO dollars, they would have to allow E to do the same thing not too long afterward.

At about this time, I decided to influence the island of CONO to come through with a counterproposal. This was to say "Yes, you are right; we should have a gold standard; the CONO dollar should be the principal island currency; the currency of E and MY should be convertible by agreed exchange ratios into CONO dollars; CONO dollars should be convertible into gold. We recognize also that the amount of gold we have is small, yet not seriously so because the dollars, not gold, will be used in circulation, in deposits, and in process of transfer. As you economic representatives of MY have said correctly, only a small amount of gold actually must be available. So, we shall be willing to transfer to MY some gold when you present CONO dollars to us. However, only a fraction of what you ask for will be granted. Thus, if you come to us with a thousand of CONO dollars and demand gold, we shall give you gold for a tenth of it."

CONO suggested one other thing, not exactly trivial, beyond what I had introduced into their minds. They said, "This is the time to set a sensible new price for gold, that is, to determine how much of it shall be considered equal to a

CONO dollar. What we have claimed in the past as the price is out of date, ancient history. Now we have a new, larger international economy. We must relate the price of gold to our real, true world's monetary needs."

So CONO created a new price for gold in 1850. They valued gold much more highly and thus devalued the CONO dollar. This was accepted by E and MY provided that the exchange ratios of E and MY dollars were simultaneously improved, each against the CONO dollar, to recognize recent CONO inflation since the last setting of the so-called "fixed" ratio. CONO had to accept this and E and MY then came into possession of a small amount of CONO's gold. Each year a little more of it passed from CONO to E and a smaller but still significant amount passed also to the island of MY. It was further agreed that if there is any "disturbance" (everybody really meant excess "inflation" on the part of CONO) to this world monetary system and the new "fixed" ratios of currency exchange, then representatives from the islands would gather again and try to figure out what to do.

In 1852, the price of gold was raised again by CONO, and the currency ratio adjusted again in favor of E and MY dollars. This gave CONO more CONO dollars' worth of gold in their reserve treasury without their discovering any more gold, a neat trick again. The act was not entirely unanticipated by E and MY, since the number of CONO dollars to be found everywhere was steadily increasing. E and MY did not like to think that the conversion of their CONO dollars into gold would bring them now less gold per CONO dollar. On the other hand, with this new devaluing of the CONO dollar against gold, the gold they already possessed could also be counted as more valuable. Private bankers on the islands of E and MY as well as those on the island of CONO all held some gold and did not object. Some who had acquired all the gold they could lay their hands on, even borrowing CONO dollars to buy gold with, gambling there would be a devaluation, were delighted. When the CONO dollar was devalued or, which is the same thing, when the price of gold was raised in

CONO dollars, they turned in some of their newly acquired gold for CONO dollars, paid off their loans, and ended with far more gold and CONO dollars net than they started with.

Quite apart from CONO's devaluations of the CONO dollar against gold, which occurred every two or three years, the islands of E and MY revalued their currencies against the CONO dollar. The island of MY changed the ratio, arbitrarily and unilaterally, of the number of MY dollars it would exchange for a given number of CONO dollars almost every year. MY's government based these decisions on the easily substantiated claim of excessive inflation on CONO. MY knew their revaluation would raise the price of their products for sale on CONO in CONO dollars. Still, they were confident they would be able to sell their merchandise there in adequate volume to give them all the CONO dollars they needed to buy the CONO products they wanted. CONO was the bad boy that had allowed inflation of its price structure, and MY was not about to produce for CONO's citizens at a lower price than was good for MY. E was a bit more reluctant to revalue for reasons we shall soon discuss, but it did so periodically nevertheless.

In this way, we find our islands expanding economically, engaged in increasing interisland trade as they entered the late 1860s. However, they were approaching a monetary crisis of major proportions.

The gold standard base I had so carefully laid out had served to give some kind of stability for a few years, surviving the several severe adjustments in the price of gold, and a number of changes in currency exchange ratios which I have already described. But what was finally being disclosed to everyone was that the monetary system was worse than inadequate. CONO's inflation did not come under control. Its prices rose. Its output fell. On the island of MY there was wealth and reasonable stability but too many CONO dollars in circulation and in the bank. They had a supply piled up that was more than they could see fit to spend for products being made overexpensively on CONO for ten years, and it was still accumulating. However, at least MY had succeeded, through individual deals made regularly, in getting larger amounts of gold from CONO than had been obtained by E. E mostly piled up CONO dollars. There were reasons for these conditions that I must now tell you about.

As E's excess CONO dollars built up in the 1860s and on into the 1870s, E's government put some pressure on CONO's government to exchange as much as possible of this surplus into gold. But E did not demand gold from CONO for every excess CONO dollar it held. It never gathered together almost all of its CONO dollars into one bundle to present them to CONO's central bank to be converted into gold. It did not try this for the simple reason that it knew the excess had become sufficiently large that CONO would simply have felt itself forced to declare a change in the rules. Actually, it would have taken all of CONO's gold and more to make a fair trade, and CONO, E was positive, would refuse to give up all of its gold to E. Of course, there was the question of what "fair trade" meant. What was the real value of gold in terms of CONO or E dollars or anything else? Surely CONO could have arbitrarily so greatly altered the price of gold in terms of CONO dollars as to pay off E in gold, using only a trivial part of its supply.

Of course, exactly this process had been taking place for years: E with too many CONO dollars, followed by pressure on CONO to release more gold, followed by CONO's changing the price and releasing a part of its gold, followed by a change in the exchange ratios of CONO dollars into E dollars, followed by a period of reduced world trade, followed by a pickup in the trade but, again, too much in one direction, with CONO buying more with its dollars than it was selling for E dollars.

Also E continued to display a strange, stubborn reluctance to recognize that the imbalance was certain to remain. Always there was the hope, conviction that it would be well not to dislocate E's production operations by any step too antagonistic toward sales to CONO. Hopefully, CONO's inflation would come under control, or, with the latest change in currency ratios, or the latest gold price revaluation, CONO's products would become more attractive and E would buy more from CONO and the money would start flowing the other way. Always there was the wishful thought that the large quantity of CONO dollars on E would be used to buy something valuable for E on CONO and everything would be straightened out.

Under urging from both E and MY, CONO's government in 1870 instituted new programs to try to stop its inflation. It exhorted the people to work harder and freeze wages and prices voluntarily. It told them of the dangers of so great a surplus of CONO dollars on the other two islands. A CONO dollar in the hands of a foreigner was a promise to pay by CONO, it was a loan to CONO by the foreigner who held that dollar that would have to be paid back by CONO on demand, if not in gold, then in something else CONO possessed. The other islanders could come into CONO with these promises to pay and buy up anything in sight— land, buildings, goods, factories, machines, services. CONO citizens were engaged in mortgaging away all of their possessions when they lived more luxuriously than they should, on credit, borrowing in this way from the other two islands, working too casually. They must change their ways.

But this lecturing did no good. Instead, there were resentful reactions. "Stop foreign goods from coming in," said Borio del Forensica, "then CONO dollars won't go out of the island, then we shall not be buying their products and they will not keep accumulating CONO dollars." He argued further that such an embargo would be a great stimulus to CONO's decaying industry that was suffering from the competition of E's lower-priced products. "We shall then satisfy our needs with our own efforts as we did decades ago, before we made the mistake of going international."

Others replied that since halting inflation was a must, the worst thing would be to keep out the cheaper foreign

goods. If low-price E goods were prevented from reaching CONO's market, then locally manufactured goods would be the only ones purchasable and they were priced much higher. This in itself would raise the average price of all goods purchased. With higher prices for most products, everyone would demand higher wages in order to be able to buy essential goods needed and the inflationary spiral would wind up, not down.

CONO had no solution to the developing crisis. It tried some curbs anyway. It increased taxes. It cut credit. It cut back on government spending and education. Transportation and public health services suffered and unemployment began to be substantial. Still prices did not come down. Wherever costs of labor and materials were so high that there was no profit in production, the supplier companies chose, naturally, to fire their employees and go out of business. Why risk the investment? A depression thus began to form on CONO. I knew that this would stop inflation and get the prices down in time, assuming the government did not start printing currency like mad as had happened decades before. However, a real depression was unacceptable politically, to say the least, so the government cut taxes and increased government projects again to be sure that everyone would be put back to work and printed money to pay for the costs.

High tariffs against foreign goods were applied on CONO by mid-1875 and CONO further instituted a ban on CONO dollars leaving CONO for investment in the other islands, allowing CONO dollars to go out only in payment for goods. The government stopped CONO banks and citizens from changing CONO dollars into foreign currency. All this made the CONO dollar look less and less healthy, and fewer people wanted to hold it in preference to gold or E or MY currency, further devaluations of CONO dollars always appearing imminent.

On the island of MY, things were not completely serene but they had less dependence on the situations internal to E and CONO. MY had, as I told you before, very shrewdly selected their products for export, developing their specialties. They were able to get good prices for them and to buy with the CONO and E dollars they thus accumulated what they needed from CONO and E, particularly from E. They were closer to self-sufficient, had not overexpanded, and operated with an essentially free market as to labor, wages, and prices. They continued to have their small ups and downs but generally their economy grew with a modest degree of inflation and only a small unemployment problem. They were not about to collapse. They were not approaching a crisis domestically.

MY did, however, regard what was building on the international monetary front in the 1870s as of crisis proportions. They evolved a plan with regard to their excess CONO dollars, the principal direct issue of the crisis for them. They were afraid to ask for a complete exchange of their surplus CONO dollars for gold from CONO. To do so would only result in either a flat turndown (and hence a breaking up of the whole international monetary system) or else a compromise of little value in which CONO would raise the price of gold, in terms of CONO dollars, so high that MY would get little gold anyway. They thought they could do better. They began using those CONO dollars to buy land, facilities, and equipment (even if it is not the most modern equipment) from the island of CONO. On one occasion MY bought 1,000 of CONO's pigs with CONO dollars. They would have bought 2,000 except that the prices rose too high during this first purchase. They bought some used sewing machines from CONO, whose apparel industry was in the doldrums. There were better machines, better manned, on the island of E where much of the clothing for all three islands was now being manufactured. However, an enterprising manufacturer of sails for boats on the island of MY, who had excelled amongst all the three islands in that specialty, had figured out a way to modify the machines so he could use them in his factory.

MY's leadership realized that there was a limit to how

much they could buy on the island of CONO with their
CONO dollars before the government of CONO would slap
on an absolute ban. In 1875, however, MY citizens owned
large sections of CONO.

On E, the situation that had been building gradually for
a quarter of a century had surfaced by 1875 as a serious economic dilemma. Here was E, with a mountainous pile of
unused CONO dollars (at any rate, a big figure on the
accounting books of its banks), with a substantial amount of
CONO's gold in its treasury, producing all kinds of goods to
be shipped to CONO, and some to MY, and being paid in
CONO dollars by both. Finally E's government determined
to act. It decided at last there would never be a reversal of
this lack of balance of payments. CONO would never be
producing goods of equal value to what E was shipping out,
goods that the island of E wanted and would buy!

E's leaders met to meet the crisis. What were their alternatives? E could simply refuse to accept CONO dollars. This
was one possibility to consider. Since E had set up its economy on a production volume so high, serving CONO as well
as E, such a step would throw E into a big depression. In
1875 E was producing metal articles, textiles, tools for agriculture, paper, seeds, ceramics, and materials for house building to almost half the total requirements of the three islands.
If it suddenly refused CONO dollars, then it would have to
curtail a large fraction of all of this production equally suddenly. What would it do immediately with all of its extra
workers? On the island of E the government was paternalistic.
A stable economy was worshipped. A steady price structure,
fixed wages, and level and high employment were all part of
the system, their way of life. Their pattern had made them
the strongest country of the three in terms of production.
They were the hardest working and the most determined, and
now also the champions of material success and technological
achievement. (And they were helping to maintain CONO at
a standard of living in many ways greater than their own!)

Of course, they considered other ways out of their dilemma. One favorite was to use their CONO dollars to go to CONO and buy up as much of CONO as they could. They knew such attempts, already tried on a small scale by the free enterprisers of MY, would bid prices up. But a worse problem with this was seen. It was not clear what they would do with CONO factories if they owned them, if CONO's people were reluctant to work, if the quality and productivity were steadily to decline.

I don't want to give you the impression that CONO was producing nothing of interest to E. CONO still had a substantial production and retained its position of strength to produce quality goods of some kinds. E, as well as MY bought some of these. But this situation had become the exception by 1875. Moreover, the general declining of quality and the higher prices of CONO products would again and again tend to make E decide that if it only waited a few years it could produce what it needed by itself and that overall this would be a better idea. So, buying had been reduced from year to year and planning to produce a broader array of products on E for its own use had become the common approach.

In certain production CONO was clearly superior and E depended upon CONO for these items. But even here there was concern on E by 1875 that it was bad strategy for the future to remain dependent on CONO. In view of the unstable international trade and monetary situation and the performance of CONO, counting on CONO to fill E's needs simply did not provide adequate security for E.

On a number of occasions in the 1860s E came to CONO with its CONO dollars and bought part ownership in production plants, particularly of goods that CONO was producing for E. This at first looked to be a good idea for E because it was a way of getting some value out of CONO dollars being collected. Also it was thought it would provide E with a measure of influence to guarantee good performance and delivery by the CONO factories. Insofar as E was an important customer for those factories, E thought it would be in a position to bring success at least to the sales activities of these companies and maybe there would even be a good return on the investment of those dollars in CONO. But this joint venturing of E investment on CONO resulted in discouraging experiences. Part ownership did not really provide very much influence and certainly no control. The E investors simply found themselves partners in ventures that seemed to be headed for decline as wages went up and quality down on CONO. Moreover, CONO government action seemed to make good management difficult.

The life on CONO, E knew, was by 1875 built on dependence on E for many necessities. CONO citizens, faced with a ban by E on accepting CONO dollars would assume, in ignorance, that E's suppliers were simply playing a game, bargaining for much higher prices, profiteering, gouging because they had developed such dominance of the market for many CONO requirements, a virtual monopoly. E had to contemplate that they would probably end up with severed relations with CONO if they took the ultimate defensive step precipitously. Sooner or later perhaps this would lead to war, as CONO would get new and more emotional leadership resulting from their economic upheavals. After all, CONO people had use of force in their blood. They were basically dangerous people.

Some E leaders suggested E should demand all the gold of CONO in return for a proper block of CONO dollars and that if this gold was not forthcoming, E should take it by force, risk war now that E is stronger. Had it not been done to them thirty-five years before? Would revenge not be sweet? Would it not be the realizing of a suppressed desire to dominate CONO?

I must say I entered into these critical discussions, using one or another voice or brain, to stop this kind of emotional thinking. Perhaps my contribution was not needed. The islands in 1875 had no real interest in going to war. But they had developed an international economic crisis. Of this, there was no doubt. Something had to happen.

On some days as 1875 was approaching, tired of worry over the true life problems of the islands, I would indulge in the privilege allowed me of remaining above it all. I would explore some impractical ideas, dream of ways to establish an easy, safe system of international monetary exchange which would encourage the maximum of free trade and free enterprise. I would invent systems that could never be implemented below, to provide for creative entrepreneuring everywhere, the greatest of freedom for individuals and businesses to do what they chose with any resources or capital they possessed or could persuade others to assign to them. Everybody would benefit because competition would reward the good performers and push the bad ones out of the way. Everyone would do his thing, and do it best for the good of all.

I asked myself how things would be if each nation possessed a substantial amount of gold. The gold, of course, would be prized, having industrial uses as well as applicability for coins, jewelry, decorative art, and a general money standard. I imagined in my indulgent, passing scenarios that there was the right amount of gold and it was used universally, that is, by all three islands as backing for their currencies. By the right amount of gold, I mean that in normal periods of economic activity, with no psychological, panic-ridden disturbances, anyone could walk into any bank with a bill in any of the three currencies and demand and expect to receive gold.

But remember, all of this was daydreaming. It depended on something nonexistent on the islands, namely, a satisfactory, proper amount of gold available to all three islands. Even if we imagine starting out with that adequate supply of gold, conveniently divided amongst the three, the gold might not remain well distributed. One island, say, CONO, which persisted over a period of years in operating with high inflation and an imbalance in trade against it, would see its gold being drained out as the other countries would return spent CONO dollars to CONO's government bank and demand gold, not wishing to hold a CONO dollar for much more than a few minutes of the day for fear it might be devalued. At some point CONO would run out of gold or have to put a ban on replacing its dollars by gold and we would find ourselves having to consider a quite different situation, namely, the real-life one on the islands below!

This daydreaming led me to a rather major question. Without something of lasting, that is, totally and permanently acceptable value (such as gold perhaps) available to all of the trading partners in an adequate amount, the social and political issues of each nation tend to affect the others in probably an intolerable way, assuming trade is important to them. To guard against the unsatisfactory feedback, it becomes necessary for the islands to set up machinery, economic rules which they all agree to obey, that in one way or another are restrictive to free trade, to the privilege I had imagined for businesses and individuals on every island to do as they pleased. Are not free enterprise, free trade, political freedom, and democracy all impaired, inhibited, limited, if there is not an active, thriving, working gold standard or a real equivalent, namely, a money base that is above government action, above politics?

I could not resist going on to try to invent the equivalent without gold. Would not "free floating" currencies be nonpolitical, constituting media of exchange in international trade responding only to the free market? That is, forget the establishing of agreed-upon fixed ratios and let the currency ratios just happen. Let each island do as it chooses with its economy, responding to its social and political pressures, inflating or not, printing currency as it chooses, providing for itself a correct amount or too little or too much money supply. Let each government exchange its currency for gold or not, as it can or will. Let everyone accept any currency at his own risk. Everyone will know he has a problem: the future value of currency he accepts. In the price a seller asks or a buyer considers paying, this risk will be allowed for as with any other business investment risk and any other aspect that typically causes haggling over prices in working out a business proposition. Any person, or business, or government that accepts currency, and does so in any way to his disadvantage, would eventually discover this and quit accepting so much of it or demand something else in return. It would be a free market, even if a volatile one, a fast track on which to run.

It must be understood that when I speak of allowing the separate currencies to float freely one against the others, I recognize that at every given moment there would presumably be some acceptable ratio of exchange. Thus, looked at from the island of MY, a CONO dollar may be suspect because of CONO's expected continued inflation. Still, anyone on E accepting a CONO dollar could ask himself what it would bring him if he took it to CONO and tried to buy something with it. He could further ask what he thought it might be worth in three months, in six months, in a year. He could ask his banker how many E dollars the banker would trade today for the CONO dollars he is considering accepting for his goods. Then he could sell his products for CONO dollars based upon his estimate of what those dollars would be worth to him for anything he wished to do with them now or in the future. Or he could take his CONO dollars or his promise of CONO dollars to be received in the future to the bank and obtain E dollars. It might require a lot of estimating and guessing (and it might be costly in terms of the risk or insurance fees paid to the moneychanger who, for that fee, would guarantee levels of later payments), but it need not end international trade and independent action by the islands, one against another.

But perhaps this is further optimism on my part, always seeking to provide a way for freedom of enterprise to be maximum. If CONO inflates, does not the island of E have to adjust to this inflation? Is not the CONO inflation automatically exported? Consider this: all of the businesses on E who sell products to CONO receive CONO dollars in exchange. What do they do with these CONO dollars in actual fact? They take them to the government bank on E (or get their

private bankers to perform that delivery chore) and exchange them for E dollars because it is E dollars that they use
on E to pay for their materials and labor. Where does the
government bank on E get all of the E dollars it needs for
these exchanges? It prints them. The careful economic planners on E find that the amount of money they print is not
totally of their own choice but it has to do with the amount
of excess CONO dollars they allow to come to the island of E.
If they try to regulate the arrival of those CONO dollars,
they are automatically regulating the amount of goods they
allow their businesses to sell and export to the island of
CONO. Even if E's government or its citizens take the
CONO dollars to CONO and get something worthwhile in
return, the annoying problem would remain that the number of E dollars in circulation amongst its islanders would
affect its own economy and its own price structure and might
make it difficult for E to buck an inflationary trend—and that
number would no longer be under E's government control.

     This inability of a government such as E's to try to
control its own economic destiny in an international trade
environment is even worse in some ways when there is a
freely floating currency and no attempt to maintain fixed
exchange rates. The free float is good, of course, because it
allows free market conditions to adjust the currency automatically and it pits the power of the free market against the
considerable power that results from political and social
factors that go on separately on the three islands. But what
results is a special kind of contest, not a true free market.

     There are speculators all over the place—businesses, in-
dividuals, and private banks. Even the government in a sense
becomes involved in the speculation. To conduct trade it is
necessary that almost everyone, or at least an important few,
be in the business of guessing what will happen to the values
of monies, one nation's against another's, as time elapses.
Either it is the buyers and sellers or it is the banks or the
brokers or moneychangers that do the speculating, one party
seeking to be guaranteed against the possibilities of unantici-

pated change and the other party seeking to exploit its expertise in anticipating that same change.

Money moves between nations as holders of these funds seek to anticipate changing exchange values or to realize the highest interest rates as those rates fluctuate between nations. The inflationary effects, the independent government actions to control interest or money supply or money flow to correct imbalances, to curb speculators, to regulate banking—all of these factors are thrown in, one against another in a confused, dangerous inefficient and trade-deterring market that is nowhere nearly as free as the words "free floating" on the currency exchange ratios might suggest. In the end, no one is happy, the governments who are trying to provide for their citizens, the businesses that are trying to show return on an investment, or the individuals caught up in the maze of overlapping, conflicting national forces and selfish interests.

I realized that the islands, under the pretense of, or attempt at, "fixed" ratios, had essentially tried the "unfixed" or "floating" exchange. Free market forces, government actions, and other factors kept pushing the fixed ratios into unscheduled changes—which is the very essence of a free float. Now perhaps a true, that is, a deliberate and admitted free float would be different. Maybe free market aspects would exert more influence and other factors, such as political ones, less. Maybe speculation as to adjustments, government efforts to control the speculation, and the speculators' efforts to control the government would be weaker. But I doubted it.

I concluded if the three islands were going to carry on trade and yet not be able to make gold universally available on demand in exchange for their currency it would inevitably turn out that social, political, and economic problems of one island would quickly translate into a problem for another island. Regulations, tariffs, half-free and half-handicapped trade formed the pattern in 1875. It stemmed from all kinds of local emergencies—to protect an industry from being swamped by imports from outside, for example, check speculation, or to keep the money supply under control if too much funds commenced to cross borders. It was difficult, I could now comprehend, for a perceptive person to take a position advocating something he wanted, unrestricted international trade in a free market, if he did not see how to attain it. The wise E men meeting to make crisis decisions in 1875, or all the wise men on the three islands together did not see how, nor did I, to set up a permanently healthy, free trade monetary system.

Except, that is, for the idea of a single currency and a single control of the money supply—now that would really change things.

Chapter XVII

Monomoney

As 1875 ARRIVED and the E government pondered what drastic steps to take, interisland economic relations worsened. The CONO government, without notice, applied an absolute ban on shipping any further gold out of the country. CONO citizens, businesses, and private banks were forced to bring all gold to the CONO government bank and receive CONO dollars in return. The central government bank refused any longer to exchange CONO dollars for gold. CONO inaugurated a very high tariff on all goods coming into CONO from E and MY to ameliorate the condition of CONO's production businesses who argued their problems were the result of too much importing into CONO from foreign competitors. CONO even emulated E and instituted wage and price controls of great severity in an all-out effort to curb inflation.

Both E and MY countered by floating their currency against CONO dollars. In fact, they said that henceforth their government banks would not exchange their currency for CONO dollars at all. Let everyone trade in CONO dollars at his own risk, according to his own judgment, his own guess as to what CONO dollars might bring him in the marketplace. Together, these steps, while not obliterating interisland trade, knocked it way down. Many deals about to close were canceled because the buyers and sellers did not know in what currency to set their deals or exactly what the pricing would mean some months hence when the goods would be delivered. The brokers' fees by the private money traders became suddenly horrendously high. Some of these international moneychangers went out of business as their commitments were seen to be out of line with their potential ability to pay off.

E sent emissaries with a large fraction of its CONO dollars into CONO to buy up interests in various businesses and land, driving CONO prices way up on such resources, raising havoc with CONO's attempt to hold down prices. This E action cut down somewhat on the oversupply of CONO dollars in E's hands.

On CONO, the political leaders first hailed this step by E, the bringing back of CONO dollars to CONO, as a great achievement by the government of CONO, proving the soundness of the CONO government's strong action. At least, during that short period when the CONO dollars were returning as E was making purchases in CONO, the net outflow of CONO dollars was actually in CONO's favor—that is, the balance of trade accounts, the settling of the books that showed the money transfers between countries, indicated that more CONO dollars were coming in from E than were going out. If one did not know the whole situation, one might assume that things were rapidly getting better. The nice balance of trade that everyone was seeking on CONO was beginning to be formed after all of those years. A political leader said, "Yes, E has waited a long time to take these accumulated CONO dollar reserves, our IOUs, and cash them in here on CONO for something to wipe out the debt, but now they are doing it."

However, as it was publicized, with exaggeration of

course, that E was becoming the "owner" of CONO, resentment on CONO stopped the E action. In alarm, CONO passed laws forbidding further foreign purchase of CONO resources. Whereupon the CONO dollars quit coming back in to CONO.

E also made more changes quickly. It accelerated the changeover of its industry to products that would improve the island of E. E began to schedule better housing (and even pleasure boats) for their people, along with cutting the work week and providing mass retraining and industry reconversion programs.

The government budget for sponsored research and development was doubled. They invested in a crash technological effort, for example, to complete development on an interesting embryonic idea, a motor that could provide mechanical power in factories and mills by the burning of petroleum. They put money also into building larger ships, exploring further the adjacent oceans, broadening educational programs, creating more chemists, metallurgists, mechanical engineers, and physicians.

These developmental activities began to use talents and physical resources which would otherwise have produced goods for CONO, which CONO could pay for only in almost unacceptable CONO dollars.

But the three islands' economies were still tied, one to another, too closely for a satisfactory cure of international trade problems to be based on a return to isolation. The souring of the economy on CONO continued. It became more difficult for the government of E to plan and control its economy with the deteriorating international trade situation, and the absorption of the impact of so drastic a step as almost having to stop its exports to CONO. The free enterprise island of MY began to develop sluggishness in its business as confidence in international trade was diminished.

It was clear to me, and I am glad to say it was clear also to most of my children on the islands, that something more fundamental had to be done than simply working from crisis to crisis. Ragged, interrupted, diminishing, if not sharply curtailed, island-to-island trade, contracts and arrangements that could not be counted on, economies working only at part of their potential—all this was no way to progress. The three islands, having found one another, with their advancing technology, growing populations, and all the benefits that nature had given them, should have been happy helping one another, increasing their standards of living in parallel, exploring, and maturing socially. Instead, they had managed to work themselves into a complex, unworkable interisland monetary and trade structure that moved ahead by fits and starts, negative actions being equal in number to sensible ones.

Certain fundamental facts simply had to be accepted and acted upon, and it seemed to me that they had had enough of confusion and foolishness. Perhaps they were ready now to accept some straight talk. For instance, surely they had to rely on a single source of supply of money for the three islands. They had to have a common currency and a single organization that would control the supply of money and bank credit and would monitor and direct interest rates at the central bank.

Perhaps you will say that when, for periods in the past, they seemed to operate successfully with fixed exchange ratios amongst their three separate currencies, they must have possessed the equivalent of a single currency. After all, if one CONO dollar is equal to a third of an E dollar, and everyone learns and accepts that, then that is no different from printing "three CONO dollars" when one prints an E dollar. Every bank or merchant will give three for one, and we are privileged to carry and use any combination of such bills in our wallets. So, what is the difference between this and a common currency?

When values of two currencies are fixed in ratio one to the other, it is, indeed, the same as having a single currency that is merely printed for convenience in different denominations. But that is the whole point; the ratio could not and did not remain fixed, not when the availability and values of CONO dollars, E dollars, and MY dollars were decided upon and created independently of one another. Social and political, as well as economic forces on each of the three islands led them to different degrees of control over their money supplies. They experienced different amounts of inflation. Thus, in time, they always ran into difficulties. It could have worked if there had been the happy situation that the inter-island variations were trivial, the inflation rate small for all, and the money supply growing for all three islands in excellent match to the real needs set by basic economic growth, growth of population, growth of productivity, sensible investment, and sound governmental tax and expenditure programs.

Certainly, the currencies could float against one another. We could shrug our shoulders, and say, "Let the trader beware," but that, we found, was at best an inefficient, costly, and trade-deterring way. At worst, it could explode if enough speculators guessed wrong about revaluations or acquired too much power and tried to influence and control or go into combat against the political forces and machinery.

Let my suggestion be specific, as I commenced to plant it on all three islands late in the year 1878. The governments of each of the three islands, I argued, should appoint representatives to sit on a council—call this the Money Council or the Economic Council or the Currency Council, I care not. Let everyone agree to give this Council certain powers over the money supply on all three islands. Be not concerned about autonomy and freedom. We would give the three islands adequate independence, knowing it to be essential to the growing, stable, prosperous economy we desire. We would let the separate governments raise taxes from their citizens to pay for their governmental expenditures. But the island governments could print no money and would be limited to spending only what they raised in taxes, or through selling bonds—no more, no less.

To go on, we would not allow the three islands to have

any barriers to trade: no tariffs or taxes on exports or imports, and no bans or laws restricting the purchase of assets by foreigners, whether land, factories, goods, or contracts for the services of people. Thus, we would make a totally free trade world of the three islands. Any citizen, business, or government would be able to buy, sell, act, and operate on any island as though he or it were a citizen of that island. He would not be able to vote for the leadership of E if he was a CONO citizen, but we would allow him the privilege of shifting to become an E citizen if he so chose, just as we would allow him to recruit workers for his factory from the three islands, or to hire expertise or transfer funds, materiel, and know-how.

Each of the islands would have government banks, but we would no longer regard them as servants of the respective island's government. Rather, we would know them as branches of the single Central Bank, the federated or Federal Bank, responsive only to the dictates of the Council. Of course, the Council would decide on the interest rates charged by these three government bank branches.

The private banks would obey rules set by each island's government. Thus, they might enjoy variations in interest rate from island to island. However, the interest rate of the government bank, which would make loans to the private banks, would be the same at all three branches. The Council would take on the task of setting the amount of reserves which all private banks would be required to keep on deposit with the Federal Bank branches. Also, the Council would determine and control the loan policies of all of the private banks, such as how much of total deposits a bank might loan out.

I mention all of these things, of course, because I was setting down the tools for control of the money supply by the new Federal Council. The Council alone would control the printing of money. There would be only one currency. We shall simply call it "dollars," with multiples and fractions thereof on paper and coins. There would no longer be the adjective, "CONO," "E," or "MY," in front of the word, "dollars."

I can tell you more about the detailed rules that I proposed, some of which, frankly, I had not clearly worked out in my mind when I started to sell the idea. When I had taken over the voice and the brain of a spokesman, I was quickly on the spot and had to continue the discussion under pressure from alert questioners. This forced me to some ad libbing that was not always consistent and sound, I am afraid. But I think I got my main point across: control by the new Federal Council of the money supply and of things that impinged on it. I kept talking about leaving to the three autonomous states everything else, though nothing, I hoped, to interfere with the singleness of control that I felt was essential.

Gold? Placing my faith in the Council's competence, knowing how many wise and sincere men there were from whom to choose, it no longer mattered to me whether the gold sitting in the vault was to be considered as a base for the money supply. As long as the three states accepted dollars for taxes, and the money supply and governmental budgets and taxes were intelligently selected, we no longer needed the gold. So, as an extra, provocative (but, perhaps I should confess, hopefully enticing) idea thrown in with the rest, I suggested that the gold coins be melted down and jewelers be allowed to purchase the gold for whatever price they bid on a free market and start making jewelry of greater beauty than the islands had known. Of course, it was pointed out to me that I had missed the fact that gold was believed to be valuable also in certain industrial processes and precision instrument devices, and it might accelerate these beneficial applications to allow it out of the vaults.

Do you believe I was primarily after stability of some sort in international trade, the eliminating of the unacceptable negatives of the variations of money supply and inflation, and government tax and spending policies on the three islands, when I pressed for my Federal Council? You are half right. I was also intent on getting optimum economic growth, my stubborn old aim.

By minimizing the Council's role in most matters of life, I hoped to suggest that there should be considerable freedom for every activity except monetary control, for everyone to do as he chooses. As long as a man could borrow money to expand his business, his and his banker's judgment both saying that there was high probability he would pay back the loans and have additional profit left over, the federal government should not stand in the way. After the Council has set the limits on the money supply, and the basic interest rate at the Federal Bank which was corollary, they should not go on to supervise the use of money.

Similarly, if any one island state had a big expenditure program, this would mean its taxes would become high. Each island should make its own decision as to whether it wanted more economic growth, more industry, or more government services for all of the people, paid for, presumably, by the government budget. Let the people decide whether they wanted better roads or schools or more individually owned houses.

It took me months to carry out my campaign of thought control, but I had guessed correctly that they were ready for it. My ideas were sound and they needed them. Of course, there were doubts on all sides, from business and government leaders, labor leaders, educators, and housewives. Nationalism had its many days. Each island wondered what the monomoney idea would do to its position vis-à-vis the others. How much autonomy would they lose? Would their growth be stymied while the others would gain advantage?

I had anticipated these worries in my arguments. If in truth my plan was better for E, let us say, or for MY as compared with CONO, then those on CONO who thought so could take their worldly means and belongings and shift location. Individuals and businesses could move about, become residents of or operate on the other islands, or invest their funds there. Or, if production should fall on CONO and there should be fewer jobs there, then labor could shift to E, where the jobs could be found. The labor leaders could go to E to peddle their campaigns to organize labor.

An island which for any reason could be considered at a disadvantage would have to mend its ways. Know-how, at least, could be transferred about and anyone on one island could, in principle, enjoy the products wherever they might be manufactured on all three islands without concern about paying a penalty because it originated on another island. If E's strict control of wages and prices should make it more difficult to produce or to sell products there, then presumably they would be forced to adjust their wages and prices to meet the competition.

I had given the islands much more than a free, international trading market. I had outlined for them the minimum of federal control necessary to avert the handicap to trade of deviations in inflation and other aspects of their separate economies, and I had left the rest of it to the states. Each island could take care of its unemployed as it chose. If one island was overly generous in unemployment relief, then it could be expected that the unemployed from other islands would come there to enjoy the benefits. Its budget then would be depleted and it would be forced to a program of providing less relief.

I was confident that my plan would come close to guaranteeing to the islands that they would have that growth which they wanted to have, with a minimum of dislocations. My free market bias was showing, I admitted to myself, but surely no Council would be so conservative or unimaginative as to hold back the supply of money and thwart economic growth. People still would be put out of work if some specific businesses or industries or trades expanded too rapidly and then had to contract. Technological change could bring dislocation. But, in addition to automatic, free-market, compensatory forces, the three islands' governments should be expected to help with programs tailored to speed adjustment and cushion the downward swings or brake the overly upward ones.

I have described this as I felt it, enthusiastically. Perhaps, however, I have given you the wrong impression that I thought I had the answer to everything. I knew I did not. As I have indicated, I was led ahead somewhat by my own rhetoric. I was confident of part of it, and I was interested in how the rest of it might work out. But there was one facet to what I proposed which I had not fully comprehended and perhaps should have. I did not see it until some years later, after the system had been in operation for a number of years. (No, on second thought, I half perceived the issue and perhaps I bordered on being deceitful when I talked the islanders into this system without bringing that issue up. They did not anticipate it and, when it dawned on them gradually, they felt they were taken in. They had no one to blame, not knowing I was involved. I both did and did not feel a party to the deceit. I could have brought it up as I began to understand the problem, while I was selling the plan, but if I had, then I know the plan would not have been bought.)

It is time for us to discuss the matter. The issue is the political unity of the three islands. Inadvertently, when they took the step of creating a common currency, or more especially, a single point of control of the money supply, they also committed themselves to become a single nation, although they did not realize it for years.

Chapter XVIII

One World

AFTER THE CREATION of the Economic Council, the state governments—that is, the governments of the three islands—soon began to be aware that their most important task was the appointment of members to the Federal Council. Other island government duties became largely administrative or dealt with smaller local issues. Everything of a grand policy nature that the island governors wanted to tackle always seemed to come back to whether the economy could afford it. State government expenditures, versus taxation, versus economic growth—all seemed to depend upon the actions of the Council at the federal level.

Business and industry became multinational or, if you wish, multiisland. The states could tax businesses and private citizens on their islands, but they had to be careful to choose a tax plan consistent with interisland trends over which they had no direct control. Too high a tax, and business or population might move and operate elsewhere. Too low, and the island government would have to cut expenditures, no longer having the money-producing privileges of old. Generally, the separate islands had to manage carefully and cooperate or else all matters relating to money were decided by the Council—and money matters were important.

The Federal Council gradually increased its influence over the life on the three islands, at the expense of the scope of authority of the island governments. For instance, it became apparent that certain uniform laws were needed to regulate what business and industry could do on the island group as a whole. Businesses could operate freely between the islands, investments could be made everywhere, and people were permitted to move about. However, the separate islands each taxed their people and businesses and spent the money on the interests of the individual islands. Who was to say, E or MY, whether the income of a business or a man, the results of his operating on both islands, was to be taxed by one or both islands and, if divided, in what proportion? A federal law was needed for this.

What if CONO wanted to use state funds to subsidize an industry whose health or growth CONO believed to be essential to its economy? Was that not unfair competition against E operations in the same business? If CONO's government forgave taxes to a leather producer to help him stay in business as he competed against an E leather producer with lower wages, was that not the same as if CONO had put a tariff barrier against E's leather goods, a forbidden state action? What should be uniform as to regulations over the islands and what need not or should not be, and who would decide? Clearly, the islands would have to decide as a group and agree to abide by a group decision or else they would be back to economic warfare and economic isolation.

Note, as an example, a concern with monopoly which arose and needed federal attention. No one business enterprise, all agreed, should be allowed to become so great as to put all competitors out of business and then be able to control prices. It was clearly not good for the public to destroy free market competition and to allow owners of a private business to dominate consumer access to specific, necessary categories of products and services through monopoly control. Most large companies were multinational and, in a free trading community of states, a true monopoly threat could only come from an enterprise that had taken over the entire market over the three islands. Only federal laws and action could handle antimonopoly control.

A good illustration of this is found in the history of the Barona Beer Company. On the island of CONO, Bitero Barona had set up a monopoly on the production and selling of beer as early as 1770. His was a good beer then, although very similar to the several other light alcoholic drinks produced on the island. He acquired his monopoly position by a combination of various skills and schemes.

First, he sold his beer at a good profit, being a somewhat better brewer and businessman than his rivals, and managed to use his savings to buy out a few of the weaker competitors who were losing money and facing eventual bankruptcy. Having now a substantially greater sales volume, and with other beer specialists working for him, he was able to lower his prices while maintaining his quality and his profit flow. His remaining competitors, individually, sold less beer, produced smaller batches, and so found that their purchased materials, production, and distribution costs were higher per jug. They made only a little profit while he made a great deal. In fact, he was able to buy out the others by offering them attractive prices they could not refuse.

By this time, he was in debt, having borrowed to make the purchases of his competitors. He took in a number of partners, selling to each of them little shares of his company on the promise that, after using the money he so raised to buy out his competitors, he would raise his prices and make more profit. Then they, as partners, would find they owned shares in a more valuable piece of business property than when they bought in.

Barona then began to speak of lower anticipated profits for the period ahead, instead of higher ones, claiming he had been a bit optimistic in some of his assessment of costs. This was enough to cause some of his bankers to become uneasy about their loans to him. When the rumors of bank loan problems were spread around, as he knew they would be, particularly with his help, he was able to buy out his partners' shares and have the business all to himself again. At this point, he increased prices and began to reap high profits.

He was careful to keep his output level so as to hold the price of beer high. But sooner or later these high profits and the unfulfilled demand had to become known, and this was a signal for competitors to enter the beer business. He tried to maintain his power by buying up his rivals, but this became increasingly expensive, as he reckoned it would. At about this time, he heard that the government was considering a law against monopoly, so he laid plans ahead. When the law was passed, he was prepared to take advantage of a special loophole. He convinced the government that competition amongst beer bars and producers would most certainly cause overdrinking and be "bad for the moral fiber" of the island, and that only one highly reputable dealer should be licensed by the government to engage in the trade, something the law allowed when good morals were threatened. The government bought the idea of government licensing for beer, but it licensed two others as well. They could not compete successfully, so they went out of business, while Barona, still having the lion's share, kept the prices up, enjoying the profits from a continuing monopoly within the law. Of course, CONO's antimonopoly laws were inadequate or Barona would not have maintained its monopoly.

After the trade started between the islands, Barona Beer began to be sold on E and MY and quickly became the most popular drink on those islands as well. Bitero was now long gone, but his successors had maintained the monopoly position for beer manufacture and sale on CONO. In little time, E competitors duplicated the CONO-based Barona Beer at a lower price, what with their lower labor rates, and the E beer began to appear also on CONO and MY. The CONO government was delighted, because they had been trying to break the Barona monopoly for years. Then everyone found out that the E beer companies had really been started by and were owned by Barona, a perfectly legal situation on E. By then, the need for federal antimonopoly rules was apparent.

The Council, when originated, had been thought of as dealing with money matters, and with economic planning, banking, budgets, and taxes insofar as these matters related to money supply control. However, the Council became the logical vehicle for expansion to include the additional federal duties of the making of federal laws. It started with rules for smooth interisland commerce and trade. Then the Council added regulation of transportation facilities between the islands, and then communication, then the setting of controls on types of taxes that could be levied by the three islands on their businesses and citizens. It went on to the eligibility of citizens for unemployment relief and social security, old age benefits, and, finally, voting privileges for those who moved from one island to another.

By 1890, I was not surprised to note that the Council had set up an expenditure budget and declared a federal tax on all business and individuals on all the islands so as to raise the funds it needed for its spending. The Federal Council became almost too powerful. Clearly, a group of Federal Councillors, with money raising, printing, and spending privileges, and able to direct banks, businesses, and private citizens on numerous dimensions of life, could be absolute dictators. Where were free enterprise and democracy in all of this?

Even as it began, this concern of mine started to fade, because its birth was followed rather swiftly by ideas and actions by the islands to make the Council the intended servant, not the master, of the people's wishes. In 1891, the state governments no longer simply appointed people to the Federal Council, now a broad entity for lawmaking, judging, and implementation, nor were the councilmen appointed for life. These important government leaders were henceforth elected by the people and stood for election or reelection every few years.

By 1900, while there was a good deal of continuing and vociferous complaining about states' rights, the three islands began to think of themselves as a nation. It was a single world of which they were all members. Uniform laws and controls applying everywhere coexisted in a gray, consistent balance with delegation of authority and autonomy to the individual islands. When I last went down to enter into discussion on this matter of a single nation versus three autonomous islands, the question of balance was still being argued and adjusted, and I suspect that it still would be if it were not for occurrences in 1940.

Chapter XIX

Diseconomics

IN THE DECADES just before the arrival, in 1940, of the United States Navy, two general topics dominated the street-corner discussions, the deliberations of the wise men, and the political campaigns on E-CONO-MY. One of these always appeared serious to some, never lost the interest of any of the islanders as a topic of conversation, but became, as 1940 approached, as much a vehicle of facetiousness as of rational and constructive thought. The other started out as a bit of futuristic, theoretical speculation, and developed to become the frontier field for high-priority, urgent, practical action.

The first of these was the continuing argument about states' rights versus the authority of the federal government. It did not matter what the detailed facet was; a problem and at least two persons to argue about it were always available. The commonest complaint was that federated control of the three islands had been usurped to an extent counter to original intentions. Some wanted a turning back to autonomy for each island. This kind of talk became more and more foolish, because the islands in the 1900s were irrevocably linked with one another. It was no longer very important to be a citizen of a specific one or another island, at least not for most people. Only a few aging reactionaries equated to disloyalty the tendency of members of the younger generation to take up life in some spot other than where their families originated.

The islands progressed (some would say struggled along) with a hybrid of free enterprise and governmental control. Of course, tariffs, trade imbalances, and international monetary systems were no longer problems. All that had been cured with the single monetary system and the single point of money-supply control. Economic growth had its ups and downs. Unemployment was often higher than desired. Inflation continued to be annoying, at times, but it no longer created an international disturbance.

Though I followed their economies in great detail, I still cannot tell you the precise amount and nature of governmental control of the economy that is best. One reason I cannot give you that answer has to do with the second issue that took over the islands' interest in the 1920s and 1930s. The goals of the society were changing rapidly during this period—this, in an economic, but more especially in the broader, total social sense. How can I speak intelligently of the proper role of government, federal or state, in planning for and control of economic growth when I am not any longer so certain as to what to include and count when I make a list of the items in the economy that are growing?

For example, is leisure a valuable item, something produced by the economic system like houses or food? People valued leisure, I noticed. In fact, its value was rising higher and higher on the islands. A man would always be expected to choose a job based on its content and opportunity for improvement. He would weigh the wages he would receive and consider the location of his employment. But he also would now evaluate the job from the standpoint of leisure time available. Not only would he value time of itself, but he would rate the value of anticipated hours of leisure by surveying his access to facilities or means to utilize those hours. Suppose the economy produced less of the usually measured products or services this year than the previous one but it increased the hours of leisure per person. Is that a gain or not? What do we or should we want and measure in accomplishment per person, more shoes or more hours to walk barefoot on the beach?

Now, to get into the heart of the issue that came to command first priority on the islands, I must report that by 1920 it was beginning to be noticed that many of the previously beautiful, freshwater streams flowing down into the ocean, once filled with fish, were now barren and foul. Fresh drinking water could no longer be obtained from these streams, and they were in some ways less than usable for industrial plants without prior processing of the water. No one would enjoy walking up and down along the streams, nor would he catch any fish if he did.

The waters had become polluted because of too much dumping of sewage and industrial waste into them. So, when I assess economic growth, is it proper for me to count the added production of industry along a waterway and not subtract from it the loss of the freshwater stream, a resource that the islands used to possess? There is positive economic growth to judge and plan, but there is also the negative or diseconomics growth to consider.

Part of my problem of understanding how to do sound economic planning in their society when it reached an importantly high level of diseconomics was the difficulty of seeing the free market relationship to it all. If everyone paid for air and water for his own use and such a necessity were furnished competitively at the marketplace, then perhaps I could go on thinking about these things in my habitual style. Air that is free from the fumes of the burning of oil and that contains no acid vapors from a nearby industrial process would bring a higher price. If someone owned that air, it would be in his interest to keep out the pollutants. At least he could compare the cost of his arranging to have air to sell of various degrees of purity against the demand for it at various selling prices. The true value of curbing man's impairment of the environment against the costs would emerge in the free market. Man would have the amount of contamination or the degree of freedom from contamination that he was willing to pay for after considering what other benefits and detriments he could realize for the same price.

But, is there any practical way to pit negative, diseconomic additions against positive economic ones in the arena of the free market? Perhaps, I told myself, the government could tax or charge the polluter, then the polluter could compare the costs of adjusting his waste output against the cost of the government-applied penalties. However, with the high industrialization, much of the pollution on the islands was so intermingled as to make it very difficult to measure the contribution of and hence the charge to individual polluters.

Every home, school building, government office, bank, and factory used oil lamps. With the population density at the 100,000 point on the three islands, this oil burning of itself created a dull beige cloud enveloping the people at almost all times. The oil burning from industrial processes added a thicker brownish component, competing with exhaust gases of many hues and odors from numerous metallurgical and chemical operations. The undesirable ingredients in the air seriously affected the health of the citizens according to physicians, slowed down the productivity of workers, and handicapped all food-growing whether of grains, vegetables, or pigs. The polluting of the oceans with waste was requiring the fishermen to go out farther to find fish, fewer and fewer of which wished to come close to the islands. All this added to the cost of fishing. Negative contributions to the economy were clearly growing rapidly, even though it was harder to count them up and figure a way to charge for them than for the positive items of food, clothing, shelter, and the rest.

By the 1930s, the islands had reached a crisis with regard to the ruination of the environment. Diseconomics began to be talked of with respect and fear, and simply defined, narrow economic growth was an increasingly less revered concept. Unless the negative as well as the positive aspects were integrated, difficult as doing that appeared, the whole idea of economic growth was seen to have doubtful value. Worse, preoccupation with it in the old sense was felt to be dangerous.

The realization that something had to be done about the environment came hand in hand with other new and frightening understandings. One was the growing shortage of resources. To provide the oil needed by industry and consumers, it had become necessary to dig deeper and deeper for it. This digging was done by harnessing motors that were based upon the burning of oil. It appeared that the point of diminishing returns was being reached. In not too many years, the amount of additional oil that could be recovered by going deeper would be comparable with the amount of oil used up to drive the drilling apparatus, to fuel the furnaces of the oil tool, pipe, and container producers, and to provide energy for distributing the oil.

A confusing aspect of all of this was the impact of further technological development. The great breakthrough in providing mechanical rotational energy through steam and gas turbines driven by oil-burning gas generators made possible the production of many more metal products. Rounded shafts could now be formed on fast lathes, leading to superior vehicles and machines involving rotating devices. Food production and preservation were improved as a result of the availability of better apparatus and methods and the production of specialized chemicals. Technology seemed always to lead not only to higher production and a higher standard of living, but also to the need for a higher production to provide all of the basic components of that new higher production. Each year saw more books, better education, and improved communications—but, needed to back this up: higher rates of paper production, requiring the generation of more of the basic materials for the paper and adding to the waste in the oceans, the land, and the sky.

The most disturbing new reality to be faced was the need for limiting the population. The islands had for almost two hundred years enjoyed very high growth in population. Now, everybody realized this growth had to be brought to a near halt. Every problem of resource shortage, whether it was minerals or oil, fresh water or fresh air, fish, or land for farming, was being made increasingly and unmanageably more severe by the rising numbers of human beings to be accommodated.

Granted, in theory great technological breakthroughs might conceivably occur to get around every difficulty. Foolish activity could be stopped by law. Priorities could be set on necessities and luxuries. The way of life could be altered and refined to put first things first in adjusting to the crisis. However, assuming optimistically the greatest of social advance and of discoveries in response to a massive effort in pertinent scientific research and technological development, still not all of the limitations would be abolished as if by magic. Sooner or later—and probably sooner, since they appeared to have reached a virtual ceiling on containable population already, without warning—the population growth would catch up and defeat them.

They did not want the population to be limited by natural forces that would certainly set in to counter overpopulation, namely, impaired health, lower longevity, and general misery in human relations. It was plain now that economic growth was meaningful to them no longer as a total, but only on a per capita gain—production of needed goods and services, yes, but also leisure, happiness, health, social vitality, enjoyment of environment, all rated and included.

High growth, they realized, was not synonymous with high welfare. Growth is achieved only through sacrifice of some kind—current consumption, stock of resources, environmental preservation. The government could pass a law requiring everyone to work a ten-hour day. Growth in production might then occur, but only at the sacrifice of something, namely, more highly valued leisure and time for thought. One of the foremost challenges to the government of any growing economy is keeping growth in its proper perspective—a means, but not an end. Realizing all this, the islanders decided to limit the population growth. Fortunately, some drugs had been discovered which could aid greatly in preventing conception. The problem was to increase the production and distribution of these drugs and to educate the islanders as to the importance of their use.

By 1940, the islanders had begun to see the beginning results of an intense effort to limit population growth and attain virtually zero growth in another generation. They set up detailed actions to conserve and allocate resources carefully and to minimize pollution. The chief reason they made headway was that there was a united front. Citizens understood the problem and they wanted to cooperate. Progress would have been made, in view of this near unanimity of goals, even if no one cared whether he preserved or did not preserve a strong free-enterprise aspect of the economy in the process. However, a contribution to the effectiveness of the effort of the islands came from innovations in quantifying diseconomics and bringing free enterprise into play.

In some, though far from all, industrial processes, the government was able to set charges on the exhausting of unacceptable matter into the water, air, and land. This led to superior free-market choices, providing as a final result a better match between the cost of depollution and the value of that depollution. The government sponsored efforts to develop oil-burning devices that produced less pollution, whether lamps for the home or sources of hot gases to drive turbines for motors in factories. Everyone who used these devices was taxed by how much oil he burned, but also rewarded with a tax reduction if he turned to a more advanced process that produced less air pollutant in the process of burning the oil. Again, then, free-market choices could be made by users between paying a higher tax or investing in a more costly but cleaner technique.

A good example is provided by a small lake on MY. Lake Odorosa was abundant with fish, and the government long had made it available for public rather than private use. By the 1900s, the lake had been fished dry and was contaminated badly. No individual found it profitable to save fish for spawning, or to keep the lake clean. Each person hurried to catch fish today. He had no guaranteed right assigned to him by the government to profit by any personal investment in the lake to renew its fish. Had the property rights to the lake been private, the government realized, as it sought to understand the diseconomics problem, then the owner would have provided for adequate spawning and depollution to ensure a long-run profit on his investment in Lake Odorosa.

But how far, I wondered, can the islands go in letting private interests manage the ecology? Let us ponder this for a moment. Imagine a relaxed, laissez-faire government that makes every conceivable resource a private property and then sits back to let the free market set depollution standards. Conservation is a problem in public, but not private, forests, such a government would claim. Congestion occurs on public, not private, highways. Public rivers and lakes are polluted, while those privately owned remain clean. If an owner dumps refuse in his private lake, he suffers the consequences directly, with a loss in the value of the lake.

Again, it is not important who happens to own the resources at first, the laissez-faire government would tell us. As long as some owner possesses exclusive private-property rights, the resource eventually will be used efficiently. If the original owner is not the most efficient manager of the resource, he eventually will find it to his advantage to transfer his rights to another who seeks to purchase it, manage it better, and profit from the deal. Not only will resources tend to be used efficiently under private ownership, but they will

be transferred until they reach their most efficient user on the basis of comparative advantage, greater for the new user.

One trouble is that not all property rights are easy to define and assign. The farmer may acquire rights to a piece of land, his house, his crops, and his material belongings. But can he be given property rights to the air above his head—to keep it free from noise, dust, and smoke from the other farmers in the area? Maybe yes, but it is not practical to arrange it through the concepts of free-enterprise and private-property rights alone.

Does he have a right to dam the water in his stream and prevent water from reaching others below? Does he have a right to contaminate it? If so, how much? To require his leaving it absolutely pure is to ask the impossible. If disputes about allowable pollution arise and judges try to settle the disputes on ethical grounds, they would be in trouble. On economic grounds, however, the workings of the free market are comparatively straightforward. If the farmer does indeed possess the right to dam the stream and pollute it, even a little, then farmers and industry downstream may offer to pay him not to do either. If the water is worth more to them than it is to our farmer, he will sell out to their wishes. If clean water is worth enough to them, they will pay him to limit his pollution of it. On the other hand, if he does not have the right to dam the stream or use its water and pour waste in, and if the government does not enter to preclude it, his neighbors downstream will sell him that right if it is worth more to him. Regardless of who had the rights initially, the allocation and use of resources will end up as determined by economic, free-market trade-offs.

The islands tried to mix private and governmental control as a best technique for arriving at the optimum overall environmental control. They did quite well in combining economic maximizing and diseconomic minimizing. Making parts of the procedure private meant that the result was in response to majority citizen preferences, at least more often than if the government alone had tried to control every little aspect of pollution.

Once private property rights are defined and the legal responsibilities of all are set by law, which the islands tried to do, the other function of the government was to enforce those rights. Enforcement, unlike simple definition, was often very expensive.

It is easier to detect the theft than the thief. It is theft to steal one's neighbor's horse. It is also theft to dump garbage on his property, for it decreases his wealth, the worth of that property. When theft can be attributed to a single thief, its detection and enforcement are less costly. But what if there are a multitude of thieves? As examples, consider noise, air, and water pollution. It is easy to see the theft, but difficult to apprehend and try the thieves, for there are many of them, each contributing only a small bit to the crime.

While in some instances the costs of subduing nuisances may be greater than the damage, in severe polluting of the environment some enforcement is a good investment. When thievery is commonplace, everyone loses, not just the people who are robbed. The more likely a good will be stolen, the less it can be sold for. A plot of land, when subject to air and noise pollution, is not as valuable as otherwise. To be economically efficient, the island governments should wish to increase law enforcement and the protection of property rights as long as the cost of the last unit of enforcement is smaller than the increased value of the resources.

The islands pondered these relationships in much public discussion in the 1930s. Many laws were passed setting standards and calling for penalties for violations. Many other relationships of private and public action affecting the environment were purposely placed in the private, free-market category for more efficient response. They thus began, in the 1930s, to obtain a significant degree of pollution abatement.

They made some mistakes too, of course. In 1929, they mounted a campaign to collect funds for a voluntary program to stop air pollution. Each person was solicited to contribute willingly. But wily islanders contended that they had nothing to gain from the program. The smog did not bother them. They were all willing, however, to enjoy what they had not paid for. The islands' leadership learned that even with good cooperation, in general, a dilemma of a public good exists. It will be profitable, and hence tempting, for an individual to conceal his tastes and hope to benefit without sharing in the costs. Again, the dependence is on ethics and not on economic gain (or freedom from economic loss) . As a result, too little of the public good will be produced, and the islanders, as a whole, will suffer.

To achieve the optimal amount of public good, such as clean air, the islands needed a way to force would-be noncontributors to pay their share—their share, that is, according to the benefit they derived. The government was seen as having to become the agency to accomplish this end. It had to exert the power to force contributions from all who benefited. Payment had to be forced, not because the buyer considered the purchase worth less, but because he might have had it for nothing if others contributed while he did not.

In 1932, a test case was made of a steel plant on E that was polluting the surrounding air with fumes and noise. The plant did not bear exclusively all the costs of its production, because it did not bear the cost of the pollution. If the steel mill had been required by law to pay the entire cost of the harm to the environment, a high figure set, let us say, by some severely critical government estimators, it would have chosen to produce fewer goods and also less pollution in order to maximize its profits. Of course, in theory, the citizens, through their government's budget expenditures, could have induced the mill to produce less pollution by offering to pay for the cutback in production. Governmental action to force a change may prove more efficient in some cases than expensive private negotiations. The islands thought so and passed a law prohibiting the mill from causing any pollution.

The mill closed up almost immediately since it could

not produce with profit if it bore the expense of a total depollution program, nor did it know how to achieve it. It was seen then that a wise government should avoid laws which set ultimate, but unattainable, goals on depollution. The production of the mill was worth the cost of quite a large degree of pollution. Altering its strategy quickly, the government wrote a new law requiring only a substantial improvement as a first step, then began to try to assess the relative values of the economics and diseconomics, difficult as that was seen to be, hopeful of improved measures to come. The mill then reopened with somewhat less production than previously, and some decreased pollution as well.

The islands accomplished a great deal during the late '20s and the '30s in these critical areas. They measured their economic growth in the '30s by adding the products and services they produced and subtracting the cost of the harm done, estimated deliberately and earnestly, if inexactly. They were beginning to get a goal of around 140,000 as the peak population limit to correspond with a tolerable environment and an acceptably matched resource utilization rate. However, the islands had already passed 120,000 population and had reached highly unpleasant and economically penalizing crowding, pollution, and resource limitations when the American Navy arrived in 1940.

The Navy was led to the area, zeroing in on it through radar, as a result of an initial first observation by a Navy flyer. He was on a routine reconnaissance flight many miles from his carrier. What he observed was to him a most perplexing darkened sky area on the southern horizon at around noon. His diminishing fuel required that he turn back. After landing on the carrier, he told his superiors that what he saw was hard to describe—not like clouds, not a storm, but like some sort of combination of smoke and fog.

Chapter XX

Economy City, California, USA

IN THIS LAST CHAPTER, we no longer have the services of Cono to interpret for us the lives of the islanders on E, CONO, and MY. The reason for this loss is not entirely clear. Perhaps it will be partially disclosed if we add to our story the events of 1940 and the years just following. It was not long after the natives of the islands were discovered by the United States Navy that World War II engulfed America. After Pearl Harbor, the United States had to make all its decisions to reflect the winning of the war as the first priority. This resulted in our islanders being moved in 1942 to federally owned land in the mountains of California, where they quickly became a new group of Spanish-speaking Americans, with a city of their own, Economy City, California. The islands, situated where and isolated as they were, formed a site so advantageous for a crash program of ballistic missile testing and antiballistic missile defense research, both involving nuclear effects, that the United States could not justify spending the additional time required to create something elsewhere which would have been not nearly so suitable.

The moving of the islanders to the new Economy City, California, was with their permission. Over the preceding year, the people of the islands were hypnotized by the sensational events of being discovered and placed in communication with the highly advanced society which constituted the world of 1940. To become a part of the most technological nation on the face of the earth (through the offered special act of Congress) and be transported into the very midst of that exciting society was thrilling to anticipate beyond anything the occupants of the islands could conceivably have envisaged. California was the home their ancestors had wanted to reach. The goal of the eventual California colony had never been forgotten. It had attained, in fact, a holy significance. To establish themselves in California was the prime hope incorporated in the wording of their folk songs and anthems.

For the older islanders, to abandon their preconceived notions that Spain and England were dominant in the outside world, certainly in Europe and in the Americas, to open their minds to how far science and invention had changed the mode of life and the position of nations, to see huge battleships on the water and planes in the skies, listen to radios, ride in jeeps, and realize for the first time how isolated they had been, and how backward—all this was a shock with no time for adjustment. The young islanders saw only opportunity for glorious adventure.

When the islanders were given the privilege of voting to decide if they wished to abandon their three little islands and become a part of the great United States of America, they voted affirmatively, almost unanimously.

But the islanders lost their spirit, something they had not realized would happen, soon after they relocated in America. No pun is intended here in regard to Cono. But perhaps it does explain why we have not heard again from him. Wherever he is, perhaps he ceased to feel needed to watch over his people. At any rate, he is no longer interested in communicating his thoughts to us.

What did the islanders do in California in the 1940s, '50s, and '60s? Very little, really, and this was the problem. Their skills were indeed backward. There was no point in E-CONO-MY fishermen, shoemakers, and textile manufacturers continuing to produce to fill their needs. Nor was it sensible for their specialists in metals, plastics, and oil, or even their steam-driven turbine motor designers and manufacturers, to attempt to contribute to the American economy. Almost everything they could conceivably do with their background of knowledge could be done or was being done by different, better, more economical approaches. Through United States government arrangements, modern housing, food, clothing, automobiles, radios, and all other necessities of life were provided to them. At first, they worked mostly in support of the experienced United States contracting crews that came to construct their houses and other facilities.

Of course, the young people went to schools, learned the English language, and made good progress. Many went into the United States Armed Forces during the first half of the '40s, and some stayed on to become officers. Many went on to college, and a few of these, when they finished their courses, returned to the California homes of their parents. The problem mostly was with the adults, ages, say, thirty-five to sixty-five, whether businessmen or professional experts. For instance, a leading E metallurgist, age fifty-five, was offered the position of a student trainee, or laboratory flunky, in a United States industrial metallurgical corporation's engineering department.

The United States government set up some war production factories in Economy City to stamp out simple metal parts and assemble electronics chassis of the less complex type. The citizens above draft age, including ex-businessmen and technical experts, could work in the factories. They also could read and try to catch up, but it was very discouraging.

In recognition of the value of their island holdings, they all had received varying but generous amounts of United States dollars. They were financially secure—just out of place and ceasing to function as a viable economic entity.

But the islanders did make one great contribution to United States and world society, though it is only now in the 1970s that a few academics and journalists have begun to realize it. This contribution was in the form of a volume written by a group of elders, wise men, amongst the islanders in 1945–50. These old gentlemen, having contemplated carefully the nature of the world from which they had been so long isolated, thought it might be of value to set down some of the experiences of the islands of E, CONO, and MY. They believed they could see building in the big world some trends they had come upon earlier in their little world. Perhaps some lessons had been learned in advance by their otherwise backward society.

With great humility and some considerable lack of confidence, they nevertheless felt they should note that the great nations of the world happened to be embarked on a course that seemingly would repeat some of their experiences—some, that is, that were not really worth repeating. They sensed that such a writing project might be largely for their own satisfaction—really an emotional outlet, an exercise in sad, nostalgic reminiscing. They fully expected their words to go unnoticed and, if discovered, to be unheeded. Their modesty was justified.

The wise men of E, CONO, and MY in the late '40s pondered the USA with its prosperity, strong currency, and ownership of most of the world's gold. It was spreading American dollars about the earth and, using its fantastic wealth, led in technology and high production know-how to plant seeds for replicas of America everywhere. The writers thought they could predict the coming of a day a mere few decades later when there would be problems of balance of trade and payment between nations. A world monetary system based upon fixed currency exchange rates and a gold

"*Que Será, será*"

standard with too little distributed gold would not work. They expected the impact of foreign trade to grow to controlling importance in the economic affairs of nations, developed and underdeveloped. They could readily envisage that the separate social-political problems of autonomous nations would create inflation dangers, chaotic currency devaluations and revaluations, and unplanned-for shifts in economic growth rates. So they wrote of these matters as they had happened in the world they had left.

They felt that they knew, and were surprised that the leaders of the world did not seem to recognize, that a single world currency with a single point of money-supply control would inexorably be required. They wrote that, when circumstances would eventually force that kind of money control on a group of nations whose economies had begun to have vital dependence on one another, political union would follow sometime afterward, whether the nations desired or recognized it ahead of time or not.

In 1950, they wrote that the world in twenty years would discover and have to face the problem of resources and energy shortages, preservation and allocation, and of population explosion, and environmental control. They predicted the nations of the world would have to learn to set goals and priorities.

By the 1970s, the elders of E, CONO, and MY who had set down these thoughts had all passed away, with one exception. The sole survivor of the writing panel of wise men, and the oldest citizen in Economy City, California, was interviewed in 1973, just before his death. His name happened to be Cono—no descendance, just coincidence, here. He was asked whether he still believed what had been written in the recently discovered and publicized works of which he had been a coauthor.

Did he continue to think that Europe would find itself with a common currency, a single point of money supply control, followed a bit later by the recognition that political unity was inevitable, followed soon after by the addition to this Common Economic Market group of the United States and all of the Americas, then Japan, followed thereafter by China, the Soviet Union, and the rest of Asia and Africa? And all this in less than half a century?

Did Cono really believe still, he was asked, now that many years had passed since these predictions had been written, that the principal preoccupation of the people of the earth in the twenty-first century would be the continuing argument about states' rights versus the authority of the World Council, while the principal occupation would be solving problems of population limiting, environmental control, and resource availability and allocation?

To these questions, Cono replied, preferring to speak in his native tongue, *"Que será, será."*